A Survey of Astronomy

A SERIES EDITED BY COLIN A. RONAN
ASSOCIATE EDITOR: PATRICK MOORE

There are already many excellent books upon elementary astronomy, and many technical works aimed purely at the expert. Books which form a connecting link between these two standards are rare. In general, the student finds that he has to pass straight from a very elementary volume on to a work which is of a high standard technically, and includes copious mathematical formulae.

The aim of the present series is to fill this gap in the literature. Some elementary knowledge has been assumed, but the general reader with no specialized knowledge will be able to follow the text, since mathematical formulae have been used sparingly and, in general, in footnotes or appendices. Some volumes necessarily make more use of mathematics than others but the reader is always taken step by step and even those without mathematical knowledge will still be able to follow the argument.

Each book has been written by an expert in his specific field, and should be regarded as a 'step' from the elementary to the technical field. Once this series of books has been read and digested, the student should be ready to proceed to more technical volumes. In addition each volume is complete in itself although, of course, the *Survey* will only be complete within the series as a whole.

The series is, then, designed for the benefit of the serious amateur and for the student. It is hoped that University students who are considering taking science degrees will find the books particularly useful.

Throughout the series the design of the volumes has been to give an up-to-date picture, indicating both present advances and also present limitations to our knowledge.

3

FACT AND THEORY

IN COSMOLOGY

by G. C. McVittie

O.B.E, PH.D, M.A.

Professor of Astronomy
University of Illinois

A SURVEY OF ASTRONOMY edited by Colin A. Ronan

Eyre & Spottiswoode · London · 1961

179933

QB 500

First published in 1961 by
Eyre & Spottiswoode (Publishers) Ltd
22 Henrietta Street, London WC2
© 1961 by G. C. McVittie
Printed in Great Britain by
The Shenval Press Ltd, London, Hertford and Harlow
Catalogue No. 6/2427/1

CONTENTS

ILLUSTRATIONS

PREFACE

I have attempted in this book to weld together the astronomical observations relevant to cosmology with cosmological theory without entering into detailed mathematical proofs. In the nature of things, the work must necessarily be an interim report because new data are continually flowing in. The main draft of this book was completed in 1960 when J. G. Bolton and R. Minkowski were discovering, through the interplay of optical and radio astronomy, a cluster of galaxies immensely more remote than any previously studied. It proved feasible to re-write certain portions of the book to take account of this new result. I have not attempted to describe every theory of cosmology that is to be found in the technical literature of today. My hope is that, by concentrating on general relativity, the steady-state theory and, to some extent, kinematical relativity, I shall have given the reader an adequate picture of the methods employed.

That the book contains defects and limitations must be, I fear, only too true. They would have been more numerous than they are had it not been for the helpful criticisms of the General Editor of the series, Mr Colin Ronan. I owe him a great debt of gratitude for his careful reading of the original manuscript, for pointing out obscurities and for his suggestions regarding their elimination.

G. C. MCVITTIE
Urbana, Illinois

August 1960

Chapter 1

THE NATURE OF COSMOLOGY

Man has always believed that the universe in which he lives could be encompassed by his understanding. His attempts to achieve this goal constitute cosmology, a discipline that has been given many definitions. One of these states that cosmology is that branch of metaphysics which treats of the character of the universe as an orderly system, of the processes of nature and of the relation of its parts. So portentous a statement may well repel the reader rather than encourage him to enter into so vast a field. However, there is a more limited meaning of the term that has come into prominence during the present century. In this restricted sense cosmology is concerned with the large-scale structure of the astronomical universe and therefore with the interpretation of the information accumulated by astronomers. It is this study that forms the subject matter of the present volume.

The astronomer contemplates a universe of matter and energy revealed to him by physical instruments of certain kinds – optical telescopes, radio telescopes and the auxiliary apparatus which can be used with them. Today, as in all earlier stages in the history of astronomy, the conclusions arrived at about the universe are determined by the character of the instruments which astronomers happen to possess and the operations that can be performed with them. Hence the universe which is nowadays studied differs from 'the totality of things' because evidence drawn from, for example, the biological sciences, religion or philosophy is usually ignored.

Indeed the 'facts' with which we shall be concerned are obtained from astronomical observation and from experiments in the physics or the electrical engineering laboratory. The 'theories' are likewise theories of physics and in particular of mechanics, which seeks to account for the way in which bodies move under the action of the forces acting on them.

It should be said at once that in cosmology, as in other branches of science, fact and theory are inextricably intermingled. Nevertheless there are two paths along which we may proceed. One is the rationalist approach, in which theory plays the dominant role; the other is the empirical, which lays its main emphasis on the facts of observation. When the rationalist method is employed, it is taken for granted that a statement is acceptable provided that it seems to be logical and reasonable. For example, it is claimed that those parts of the astronomical universe beyond the reach of our most powerful instruments must be similar to those which are accessible. To believe otherwise is said to be 'unthinkable'. Or we may maintain it to be a reasonable belief that, if we could view the universe from some point remote from the earth, our picture of the universe would be unaltered. In this method of proceeding, reliance is often placed on a variant of the 'argument from ignorance' fallacy. It is asserted that a statement is true if no observational evidence *against* it can be adduced. Thus, of necessity, there can be no evidence that the unobserved parts of the universe are different in character from those that are observed. Therefore, it is asserted, we may reasonably say that no differences do in fact exist. Again, if matter is being created out of nothing in the astronomical universe at a rate so slow that no laboratory experiment could detect it, such a creation of matter can reasonably be accepted as in fact taking place. Unfortunately, to prove that the colour of an object is not black fails to demonstrate that it is white; it might be blue or green or yellow. And what is logical, reasonable or unthinkable to one man may very well appear illogical, unreasonable or easily imaginable to another. Nevertheless the method of imaginative theorizing in cosmology has a long history behind it. In its present day form it often assumes a mathematical aspect without thereby losing its essential character. Its prosecution is useful because all imaginable possibilities are thus explored. It becomes dangerous only when it is carried out for its own sake and when observational checks are treated as of minor importance.

In the alternative or empirical method, the emphasis is laid on the observational data. Theory may now be regarded as the synthesizer and interpreter of the results of the measurements made by astronomers. Certainly, without such a theoretical nexus, the data would appear as disconnected and unintelligible facts. With the theoretical cement, they form rational systems which can be understood. But it may well be that there is more than one theory that can provide an acceptable interpretation of the data. Especially is this the case in present day cosmology, because the relevant astronomical observations are few in number and very difficult to obtain. In examining the theories employed in the empirical approach, it will be found that they have much in common with those set up by the rationalists. For example, the assumption may be made that the unobserved parts of the astronomical universe are essentially similar to the accessible portion. But this notion is no longer regarded as a logical necessity; rather is it a simplifying idea that may be accepted until the theory of which it forms a part runs into contradiction with observation. Indeed, it is not an exaggeration to say that an empirical cosmologist should view any theory of cosmology as a temporary set of relationships. He will accept a theory only so long as it serves to harmonize the data available to him. If it fails to do so, then it must be discarded however mathematically elegant, simple or logical it may be.

The peculiar character of cosmology at the present moment in the history of astronomy lies in the simultaneous existence of data that could, in principle, solve the cosmological problem, combined with the difficulty of making the necessary measurements at all. The reader of this book will find that nearly every result which will be described has been questioned. The reason, of course, is that it is the remotest objects which are of most interest when the structure of the universe as a whole is in question. The radiation from these objects, whether it comes in the form of light or of radio waves, is extremely weak on reaching the earth. Thus errors of measurement are to be expected; photographic images will be barely detectable; the records from radio telescopes will barely show indications above the background noise. Nevertheless, the measurements are being made by men highly skilled in the use of astronomical instruments. These men themselves would admit that the accuracy of their observations fell lamentably short of that attainable, for example, in the measurement of the position of a planet belonging to the solar system. These defects should be recognized; but this does not mean that the data must thereby be regarded as valueless. The proper conclusion should be that a combination of theory and present day observation can lead only to conclusions which are temporary and subject to change when more accurate data – as well as more realistic theories! – become available.*

A type of consideration that is sometimes found paralyzing in empirical cosmology arises thus: reflection often suggests that, if a certain kind of observation could be made, this new datum might lead to a conclusion very different from that which is drawn from those data that *are* available. This is, of course, a special case of the general principle that more information can alter our ideas about nature. For example, if a

* The reader is asked to keep this point especially in mind when he reads Chapter 6.

space vehicle could plunge into the atmosphere of Venus, collect some of the gases there and bring the sample back to earth, our ideas as to the chemical constitution of the planet's atmosphere might be radically changed. That more information can alter our conclusion is true, but what is often overlooked is that new data may merely confirm what we know already. In this book, therefore, we shall prefer to avoid the paralysis of indecision engendered by the consideration that future astronomers, with their ampler and more accurate measurements, may disagree with our conclusions. On the contrary, the conclusions ought to be drawn so as to stimulate further investigation.

After these generalities, let us take a brief look at the objects whose over-all organization constitutes the astronomical universe. They are the galaxies, the largest material systems which are known today. The detailed study of these objects as individuals forms the subject matter of another book in this series and therefore will not be attempted here. Suffice it to say that a galaxy consists of an organized family of stars separated from other such families by space which is probably empty of matter. The galaxies we are able to observe differ considerably in shape. When photographed as a whole, some appear to occupy a very flattened volume consisting of a central spherical cluster of stars, around which wind spiral arms also composed of stars. Galaxies of this kind occupy a volume of space rather like that contained between two soup-plates with very wide rims and placed face to face. The arms lie in the outer parts, in the volume between the rims, while the central spherical cluster of stars occupies the volume between the 'deep' parts of the soup-plates. The arms wind round the central region giving such galaxies their characteristic 'spiral' appearance. *Spiral galaxies* also contain clouds of dust and gas, chiefly in the central plane of the system, intermingled with the stars of the spiral arms. But not all galaxies are of this type. There are also *spheroidal* and *elliptical galaxies*. These seem to have no clear volume-structure in the distribution of their stars and appear to be almost free of gas and dust. There are still other chaotic forms called *irregular galaxies*.

It has been estimated that a galaxy contains a mass equivalent to from 2 to 200 *billion* (10^9) solar masses. Indeed, the sun itself is a rather inconspicuous member of one such system, called simply the Galaxy, which contains not only all the stars visible to the naked eye and all of the stars of the Milky Way, but also vast numbers besides. The Galaxy is of the spiral type, with the sun in an eccentric position near to the central plane in which also lie the clouds of gas and dust. This accumulation cuts off the light from objects beyond but, happily for astronomers, it interferes little with the radio waves which radio telescopes record.

That the galaxies are indeed stellar systems, of which our Galaxy affords one example, is a conclusion that was made possible by the 100-inch telescope at Mount Wilson in California. This instrument demonstrated conclusively that a few of the brightest, and therefore of the nearest, galaxies could be resolved into individual stars. Moreover the number of separate galaxies evidently ran into hundreds, or even thousands, of millions. It is an encouraging fact that the 200-inch telescope on Mount Palomar, constructed some twenty-five years after the 100-inch, has not changed this general picture. Nor have radio telescopes yet demonstrated the existence of distant sources of radio waves other than galaxies. Thus the largest astronomical instruments agree in presenting us with the picture of a universe populated by galaxies. The progression from the brightest to the faintest detectable of these objects also suggests, though it does not prove, that the whole system cannot be examined by our instruments. A part of some larger whole is evidently being surveyed and, even within this restricted region, only a relatively small percentage of galaxies are bright enough to be usefully studied. All that can be said of the remainder is that their barely detectable images on the photographic plate indicate that galaxies are there. Moreover the observable region is an unknown fraction of the whole universe of galaxies. Therefore at the outset we can expect no unique answer to the problem of the nature of the astronomical universe. Many different over-all pictures may each contain a restricted region that fits that part of the astronomical universe accessible to our instruments.

This general discussion indicates that we are nowadays in a position to modify, however tentatively, the definition of cosmology given in the opening paragraph of this book. It is no longer necessary to embark on that domain 'beyond physics' to which the term metaphysics refers. Ordinary scientific methods permit us to advance a little way into the realm of the galaxies even if we have to walk more slowly and more uncertainly than did the astronomers of the sixteenth century in their efforts to unravel the nature of our own solar system.

B

Chapter 2

DISTANCE IN THE UNIVERSE

One of the fundamental problems of cosmology is the determination of the distances of the galaxies. Underlying this problem however is an even more fundamental one: what is the meaning of the term distance itself? This question may be approached indirectly by asking first of all: what operations do astronomers carry out when they claim to be measuring the distance from the earth to some astronomical object? Whatever abstract or philosophical definition of distance may occur to us, it will prove to be of real interest only if it can be shown to be some quantity that can be measured. Thus it is best to begin with the operations of measurement and to deduce from them what the meaning of distance may be. We shall start with a discussion of the basic distance-problem in astronomy which is the determination of distances within the solar system.

Distance and its Measurement

It might be thought at first sight that the distance between two objects was such an obvious physical idea that there was little point in reflecting on it. Two marks have been made on a certain bar of platinum that is carefully preserved in France; the separation of the two marks defines the unit of length called the metre. If then the distance between a point *A* in Amsterdam and a point *B* in Berlin is required, all that it is apparently necessary to do is to lay the metre bar down successively, starting at *A* and finishing at *B*, and count the num-

18

ber of times which the operation has to be repeated. But if an inexperienced person were to be handed the metre bar in Amsterdam and told to go ahead he would probably be at a loss as to how to proceed. He would want to know in what direction to start out, and the specification of a direction means that some angle measured from a standard direction must be furnished. He would also want to know how to allow for the fact that he would at times be going uphill and at others down. In other words, how are the accidental errors in the measuring procedure to be dealt with? Again someone with a philosophical turn of mind might ask if the two marks on the metre bar corresponded to an immutable degree of separation between them. Clearly, if in the journey from A to B, the bar had to be passed through the centre of a blast furnace where it was vaporized, one would be hard put to it to know what to do next.

This illustration draws attention to three characteristics of large-scale distance determinations, namely, that angular measurements are involved, that errors have to be compensated for and that the persistence of the unit of distance is important. But there are other matters of equal moment. Suppose that there is a third point C, in the town of Cadiz, for example, and that the distances from A to B and from A to C have been satisfactorily measured. It may also be assumed that the angle at A between the directions in which one must set out to go to B and C, respectively, has been measured. Then is it necessary to repeat the measuring operation in order to find the distance from B to C? The answer is unfortunately yes if the geometry of the surface on which the three points lie is unknown. But if the geometry is known, then the rules of the geometry can be employed to calculate the distance BC without further appeal to measurement. Conversely, measurements of distances between a sufficient number of points – and the angles that accompany these operations – will give a clue to the geometry that must be used to describe the inter-relationships between the distances and angles. With geometry, mathematical theory enters into distance computations and, unfortunately for those who like their science to be simple, there is more than one kind of geometry. For example, the ordinary plane geometry of Euclid which is learnt at school is different from the geometry on the surface of a sphere. It is the latter that surveyors must use when they are making a survey of the whole of Europe. By this is meant that the mathematical formulae that are employed for inter-relating distances and angles in the one case are different from those used in the other.

These problems may seem to be complex, but they are far from exhausting the complications. To the best of our knowledge and belief, Amsterdam, Berlin and Cadiz are at mutual relative rest, their distances apart remaining unchanged as time goes on. This very simple situation almost never arises in astronomy, nearly every astronomical object being in motion relative to the earth. Clearly, a distance determination for a moving object is meaningless unless we are also told the time to which the determination refers. Thus two more elements are involved when the distances of moving objects are concerned, namely, we must know what is meant by the time of occurrence of an event and we must also know how the motions of bodies are governed, what the theories of dynamics and of gravitation may be. But even if these complications have been allowed for, there is an additional one that enters into distance determinations in astronomy. Up to the present, it has not proved possible for an astronomer to leave the earth and go to any of the bodies whose distances he would like to find. In this respect, he differs from the terrestrial surveyor who can, at a pinch, actually proceed from one point to another on the earth's surface. The astronomer has to rely almost entirely for his knowledge of the astronomical universe on the information conveyed to him through the medium of electromagnetic radiation, whether in the form of optically visible light or in that of radio waves. The behaviour of electromagnetic radiation in the astronomical universe is partly determined by experimental evidence in the laboratory but also very largely by a liberal use of theory. In the application to the solar system distance-problem, it can be established experimentally on the terrestrial laboratory scale, that light-rays travel in straight lines in Euclid's sense of this term. The belief that this is a property of all electromagnetic radiation and that it continues to hold as the radiation travels over the vast spaces between astronomical objects, is based on theory and a theory is something constructed by the human mind and which therefore need not enshrine some everlasting truth. It does indeed prove to be the case that this laboratory conclusion as to the nature of the paths of light-rays cannot always be sustained.

Local Distance in the Solar System

We now go on to examine the procedures that an astronomer actually employs in order to determine distances in the solar system. The famous astronomer Johann Kepler, who lived from 1571 to 1630, knew how this could be done in principle and showed how it was possible to set up a scale model of the solar system without having any accurate notion of the distances involved in terms of miles or kilometres. Suppose that Kepler came back to earth today and that we carefully concealed from him all the accumulated astronomical knowledge of the past three centuries. But suppose that he was shown how to work our modern telescopes and clocks and it was then suggested to him that he went ahead and, with this greatly improved instrumentation, repeated the observations that he had used. Kepler would no doubt begin by measuring each day the angular diameter of the sun. By methods which would be familiar to him, even if they are unknown to most laymen, he would, by measuring certain other angles at noon each day, determine the sun's position relative to the background of the stars. Note the important point that his observations would consist entirely of measuring *angles* and not at all of measuring *distances*. The changes in the angular diameter of the sun from day to day, he would interpret by saying that it was the (unknown) distance of the earth from the sun that was varying; the apparent motion of the sun relative to the distant stars, sometimes faster and sometimes slower during the course of the year, would eventually lead him to the conclusion that the earth was moving round the sun in an ellipse with the sun in one focus. He would draw on a piece of paper an accurate reproduction of this ellipse, with all the distances relatively correct but not one of them known in terms of miles or kilometres. Having completed this operation he would take each planet in turn and, again observing angles only, find that each planet moved in an ellipse with the sun in one focus, the reproduction of each ellipse being on the same scale as that used for the earth's orbit. But in all this there is one point of theory that would seem self-evident to Kepler though it would not be so to a modern mathematician looking over his work. He would take it for granted that the inter-relations between the angles he was measuring and the distances involved were those of Euclidean geometry and that moreover the light-rays reaching him from the objects he was studying travelled along Euclidean straight lines. To this day, astronomers in dealing with the solar system make, for most purposes, the same geometrical assumptions that Kepler did. The distances so obtained will be called *Local Distances* and it is this type of distance which will be exclusively considered in this chapter, even if the adjective local is not invariably prefixed to the term distance. All local distances in the solar system may be reckoned in terms of the *astronomical unit* (A.U.) which is nearly, though not quite, the same as the earth's mean distance from the sun.

Turning the astronomical unit into miles or kilometres is a separate problem. Since a scale model of the solar system is at our disposal, all that is required is the measurement of one distance in the system in order to fix the scale. To obtain this, the earth must first be surveyed and the distances between astronomical observatories determined. The base lines from which the survey starts are measured, not with the standard metre-bar, but with flexible metal tapes stretched to a given tension, and the belief that a consistent system of distance relations between points on the earth's surface can be established on such a basis depends on a good deal of theory. There must be a theory of the nature of a metal and theories of dynamics and of elasticity – here the classical Newtonian theories are employed – before the surveyors can be sure that using the metal tapes in the way they do is likely to provide an internally self-consistent network of distances. It is also taken for granted that the geometry which inter-relates the measurements is the Euclidean, the surface of the earth being regarded as a mathematical surface in a three-dimensional Euclidean space. Suppose then that the Euclidean straight-line distance between two widely separated observatories A and B has been thus established, partly by measurements and partly by geometrical calculation. A planet P being selected, the angles PAB and PBA are observed simultaneously at A and B. Again using Euclidean geometry, the distances from A and B to the planet can be calculated and the scale of the solar system determined. In this way the astronomical unit is found to be

$$a = 92,900,000 \text{ miles} = 1 \cdot 496 \times 10^8 \text{ kilometres.}$$

In all this procedure, the important elements of principle are: firstly, that all measurements are angular measurements,

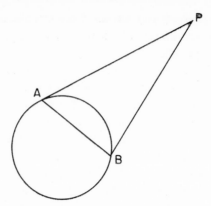

FIG. 1. Local distance of a planet.

except for the distances between the ends of the base lines on earth that are established by the use of flexible metal tapes; secondly, that calculations are performed through the formulae of Euclidean geometry; thirdly, that the paths of light-rays are straight lines in the Euclidean sense; and fourthly, that it must be possible to attach a meaning to the statement that two widely separated events are simultaneous, the two events in question being the observations of the planet from the observatories *A* and *B*.

It is not only by way of this question of simultaneity that time has reared its ugly head; our resurrected Kepler had already tacitly incorporated the notion of time-intervals into his scale-model of the solar system through his procedure of making observations on successive *days* and in successive *years*. He must have known what a day was and what a year was before he could act in the way he did. And indeed the astronomers of today introduce the notion of time into distance computations in the solar system in a much more indirect and yet fundamental way. They have at their disposal all the dynamical theory and the theory of gravitation which were first invented by Isaac Newton in the second half of the seventeenth century and whose detailed consequences have engaged the attention of mathematical astronomers ever since. As G. M. Clemence [1] has pointed out, the unit of time employed in these theories is the average value of the mean solar second during the eighteenth and nineteenth centuries, and a time proceeding at this rate is known as *ephemeris time*. The astronomical unit is then defined as the theoretically predicted radius of the circular orbit around the sun of a planet of very small mass moving at an angular rate expressed by a fraction given to eleven places of decimals. Now the Newtonian theory of planetary motion contains two very important principles which underlie the three laws of motion. These are, firstly, the postulate that all angular and distance measurements in the universe can be manipulated by the rules of Euclidean geometry and lead to an absolute distance between objects. Secondly, that there exists an absolute time. The absolute time is pragmatically defined with reference to the mean solar second during the two centuries referred to and it is one of the merits of the Newtonian theory that distance measurements and time measurements can be manipulated separately, the first by the rules of Euclidean geometry, the second, on the principle that time-intervals are not affected by the geometry that is being employed for distances. These then are the basic postulates that underlie the notion of local distance.

Trigonometric Parallaxes

It is possible to apply the method of a measured base line combined with Euclidean geometry for some of the nearer stars of our own Galaxy and thus to find their local distances. No base line on earth is long enough for the purpose, but the diameter of the earth's orbit about the sun provides one of sufficient extension. This diameter is, of course, two astronomical units in length. In fig. 2, *P* is the star, *S* is the sun and

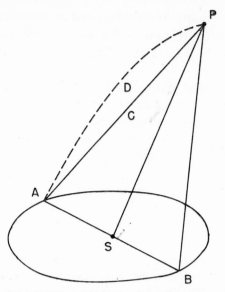

FIG. 2. Trigonometric parallax of a star.

the curve through A and B represents the earth's orbit, which for the present purpose may be regarded as circular. It is a fact of observation that there are two positions of the earth, A and B, such that the angles SAP and SBP are equal to one another. Euclidean geometry then informs us that SP is perpendicular to AB. The angle APS (or BPS) has then its maximum value and is called the parallax, p, of the star. When the parallax is one second of arc, the local distance SP is defined to be one *parsec* (pc). In practice, no star has yet been found which has so large a parallax, the nearest one, α Centauri, having a parallax of 0·75 seconds of arc which is written 0″·75. Since parallaxes are very small angles, the tangent of the angle APS is equal to the circular measure* of the angle

* The unit of circular measure is the radian which is defined as follows: Let O be the centre of any circle. From any point A on the circumference, lay off an arc AB along the circumference of length

itself. Thus Euclidean geometry and its associated trigono-metry give for the distance of a star of parallax p'',

$$SP = 206{,}265 \frac{AS,}{p''} \qquad (1)$$

because one radian equals 206,265 seconds of arc. Now when the parallax is one second of arc the distance is one parsec and AS is, of course, one astronomical unit. Thus

1 parsec$=206{,}265$ A.U.$=3{\cdot}086 \times 10^{18}$ cm.

It also follows that the distance in parsecs of an object of parallax p'' is simply $1/p$ parsecs. We shall have occasion in the sequel to use multiples of the parsec. These are the *kiloparsec* (kpc) and the *megaparsec* (mpc) which are, res-pectively, one thousand and one million parsecs. Another distance-unit often employed in astronomy is the *light-year* which is the distance that light, travelling in a Euclidean straight line at 186,000 miles per second, would cover in one year. The relation between the parsec and the light-year (ly) is

1 parsec$=3.263$ ly.

It is necessary to analyse carefully the procedure by which this trigonometrical distance of a star is determined in order to separate out what is observed from what is deduced geo-metrically. The process of parallax measurement for a star at rest relative to the sun may be thus described: a group of faint stars X, Y, Z are selected in the neighbourhood of P (see fig. 3), these stars because of their faintness being pre-sumed to be so remote that they have no measurable paral-laxes. Throughout one year the angular separations of P from each of the stars X, Y, Z, are measured. It is found that P traces out a small ellipse on the celestial sphere which reflects the motion of the earth. The maximum angular

equal to the radius of the circle. Then the angle AOB is defined to be one radian and it is easily proved that this measure of an angle is a pure number and is independent of the radius of the circle. All other angles can be expressed as fractions or multiples of the radian.

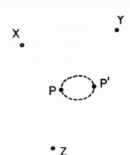

FIG. 3. Apparent displacement of a nearby star relative to distant stars.

separation of the two points PP' is then defined as twice the parallax of the star. These operations however do not imply that the geomtery of space is Euclidean or that light travels in Euclidean straight lines. The reason is that the astronomer measures only *the direction of arrival* of the light from each star at each position of the earth in its orbit. Suppose that at A in fig. 2 the light from the star P travelled along the curved path PDA, whose tangent at A was the straight line PCA. Then the observer would be unable to say whether the light had in fact journeyed along PDA or PCA. We are not, of course, asserting that light does travel in cork-screw paths; all that must be emphasized is that the direction of arrival of light at a given point does not, by itself, determine the nature of its path from source to observer. The way in which geometry and the nature of light-paths can influence the calculation of distance may be illustrated by considering the star Sirius. Its parallax is $0''.379$ and its distance calculated on the assumption that the triangles ASP and SBP (Sirius is at P) are plane Euclidean triangles is 2.64 pc. But now suppose that we harboured the conviction that PAS and PBS were spherical triangles drawn on a sphere of radius 10 pc. This would be equivalent to asserting that AB was the arc of a great circle of this sphere and also that light travelled along great circles instead of Euclidean straight lines. The rules of spherical geometry would then show that the (great circle) distance *SP* would be 2·67 pc. That the difference between this result and the Euclidean is small is beside the point: the essence of the matter is that a difference exists. Indeed, in the application of Einstein's general relativity to the astronomical phenomenon of the bending of light-rays it is precisely such small deviations from Euclidean geometry that are employed. That astronomers do not, in fact, convert stellar parallaxes into distances by using non-Euclidean spherical geometry comes about because a simpler as well as an internally self-consistent description of local distances in the solar system and the Galaxy is obtainable through Euclidean geometry. However, it does not therefore follow that this simplicity will continue to prevail when objects in the great depths of space are in question.

The base line provided by the earth's orbit unfortunately proves to be too short to give reliable trigonometric parallaxes once a star lies beyond about 100 pc or approximately 325 ly. Thus new methods must be devised for objects lying beyond this distance which from the cosmological point of view is extremely short.

Statistical Parallaxes

The stars of our Galaxy, for all that their relative positions appear fixed to the naked eye, do have measurable motions. These are revealed in two ways; firstly, by the fact that certain stars are observed to change their positions relative to their neighbours over sufficiently long intervals of time; and, secondly, when the spectra of most stars are examined it is noticed that the spectral lines* are displaced from the posi-

* A full explanation of the nature and cause of spectral lines will be found in *Astronomical Spectroscopy* by A. D. Thackeray, also in this series.

tions that laboratory experiments have determined. The change of position of a star relative to its neighbours is interpreted by saying that it has a component of velocity relative to the sun at right angles to the line of sight. This is called the *proper motion* of the star. The shift of spectral lines may be towards the red, or long wavelength, end of the spectrum, or towards the violet, short-wave, end. This effect is interpretable by the wave theory of light which shows that the star then has a component of velocity in the line of sight, directed away from the sun for a redward displacement and towards the sun for a violet. In either case the velocity component is known as the *radial velocity* of the star.

In discussing stellar proper motions and radial velocities, astronomers tacitly assume that these represent the rates of change of local distances with respect to the absolute time of classical Newtonian mechanics. Moreover local distance is identified with the absolute distance of classical theory. Under these conditions, the displacement of the lines in a stellar spectrum can be used to find the radial velocity. Let λ be the laboratory wavelength of a line which, in the stellar spectrum, appears as of wavelength $\lambda + d\lambda$, where $d\lambda$ is the change in λ. Then the displacement of the line is measured by $\delta = d\lambda/\lambda$ and it is independent of the line selected if the cause of the phenomenon is the motion of the star. The magnitude of the radial velocity v is connected with the displacement δ and the velocity of light c by the relation

$$v = c\delta. \tag{2}$$

Conversely it is argued that if every spectral line in a stellar spectrum is displaced by an amount that is a constant fraction of the wavelength of each line, then a radial velocity is most probably responsible. It will be shown in Chapter 5 that the *Doppler formula* (2) is not unique; there are other ways of connecting an observed displacement δ with a velocity.

Radial velocities and proper motions can be used to find local distances for those stars which lie beyond the range of trigonometric parallaxes. Before explaining how this is done, it is necessary to point out that a star's proper motion will greatly complicate the measurement of its trigonometric parallax, supposing it to possess a measurable one. Reference to fig. 3 shows that the ellipse PP' would be distorted if the star's position relative to X, Y, Z, underwent an intrinsic change during the course of a year. Many years of observation might then be needed to detect its parallax, even supposing that the background stars could themselves be regarded as forming an unchanging reference network.

The sun and many hundreds of thousands of stars in its neighbourhood are, it is now believed, moving roughly as a group around the centre of our Galaxy. In this large-scale motion the sun travels at about 220 km/sec in an orbit so large that one revolution takes some 200 million years. This motion of the stellar group will be ignored and attention will be concentrated on the *relative motions* of the sun and its neighbours. The radial velocities of some 15,000 stars indicate that values up to 30 km/sec are common and that those exceeding 100 km/sec are rare.* Now suppose that the subgroup formed by all the naked-eye stars is considered. These presumably are the stars that lie closest to the sun. Then it is found that the proper motions are orientated in such a way that the stars appear to be, on the whole, moving away from one point in the sky and towards a diametrically opposite one. The first point is called the apex, the second the antapex. Again, when the radial velocities are analysed, there is a preponderance of velocities of approach for stars near the apex and of recession for those near the antapex. An obvious interpretation of these phenomena is that the sun itself is in

* It is these high velocity objects that reveal the large-scale motion about the centre of the Galaxy.

motion towards the apex and this is the one that has been adopted.

The qualitative description of the solar motion has to be made precise if the speed of the sun towards the apex is to be found. The speed must be relative to some frame of reference and, at first sight, there is no definable frame. However, it is evident that the group of stars will have a centre of mass which, for the present purpose, can be regarded as moving in as gigantic an orbit round the centre of the Galaxy as does the sun. For intervals of time on the human scale it therefore proceeds in approximately a straight line at a constant speed. It is then a plausible assumption that, relative to a frame of reference with origin at the centre of mass and moving with it, the stellar velocities will be randomly distributed both in magnitude and direction. The vector sum of these velocities* will thus be zero and if this is so a detailed mathematical analysis of the proper motions and the radial velocities of the group of stars leads to the exact location in the sky of the apex. It also produces a value for the solar motion which amounts to 20 km/sec. At this speed the sun happens to travel in one year through a distance twice as great as the diameter of the earth's orbit. By waiting long enough therefore a base line of as great a length as desired is obtainable.

The solar motion has thus been found relative to a frame of reference defined by a certain group of stars. It is obviously possible to change the group and, for example, to substitute for the naked-eye stars all those visible in a telescope of some pre-selected power. There is no reason to assume that the solar motion for the new group will necessarily be identical with that found from the old. That the apex and solar speed deduced from different groups of stars are very closely similar, is evidence that the stars in the sun's vicinity form an orga-

* That is, the sum of the displacements in unit time taking into account direction as well as magnitude.

nized whole. Their motions round the centre of the Galaxy possess a systematic character and are not chaotic. Nevertheless we are presented here with an elementary example of relativity: the way in which a body – the sun – is found to move depends on the frame of reference to which its motion is referred.

The solar motion could be employed to find the distance of a star provided that the star was known to be at rest relative to the selected frame of reference. In fig. 4, S and S' are the positions of the sun at the beginning and end of a year as it

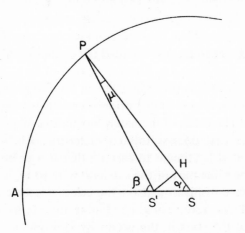

FIG. 4. Secular parallax of a star.

travels towards the apex A. The distances of all stars are so enormous compared with the size of the earth's orbit that, for the present purpose, sun and earth may be regarded as coincident. Since the star P has by hypothesis no intrinsic motion of its own, its proper motion, μ, on the celestial sphere is entirely due to the change of position of the sun. The distances $S'P$ and SP of the star from the sun are so large that one can put $S'P=SP=l$, l being the distance of the star. The angles

C

α and β are also approximately equal. If then $S'H$ is perpendicular to SP, it follows from the rules of Euclidean geometry that

$$\mu = \frac{S'H}{l} = \frac{S'S \sin \alpha}{l}$$

and therefore the local distance from sun to star is

$$l = S'S \frac{\sin \alpha}{\mu}.$$

From this the parallax of the star is obtained by dividing the astronomical unit a by the distance l and so

$$p = \frac{a}{l} = \frac{a}{S'S} \frac{\mu}{\sin \alpha}.$$

A parallax so determined is called the secular parallax of the star.

The catch in this procedure lies in the initial assumption that the star is intrinsically motionless relative to the frame of reference. There is unfortunately no means of picking out those stars that possess this characteristic. All is not lost however: it is legitimate to assume that if a group of stars lying in the same part of the sky as P were to be considered, their average displacement on the celestial sphere during a year would be zero. Thus, combining the observed proper motions of the stars in the group by appropriate statistical methods, an estimate of the distance of the group emerges. It is called the statistical parallax and it has been applied to groups of stars whose average distances from the sun run up to 500 pc.

Intensities of Interstellar Lines [2]

The spectra of hot giant stars contain relatively few spectral lines. It is however noticed that the spectrum of a star of this type sometimes contains fine dark lines. These 'stationary lines' do not share in the displacements that are manifested by the star's own lines, displacements that arise from such causes as a radial velocity, the rotation of the star as a whole or the orbital motion of a double star system. The physical interpretation of the stationary lines is that they are produced by gaseous material lying between the star and the observer on earth. The light from the star passes through the interstellar gas in the course of its journey and it is there that the stationary, or 'interstellar', lines are produced. Calcium, sodium, potassium, titanium and iron atoms have been detected in the interstellar gas as well as hydrocarbon and cyanogen molecules. The main constituent is however hydrogen. Clearly the more gas the light has to traverse, the more intense will be the interstellar lines, and therefore the intensity of the lines should give a measure of the distance of the star. This is true, provided that the gas is evenly distributed in space; by making this assumption, astronomers have put on a quantitative footing the relation between intensity and distance. However, two obstacles stand in the way of any great accuracy being achieved in this way. In the first place, the interstellar gas, though it occupies a fairly thin stratum extending to some distance on each side of the central plane of the Galaxy, is far from being uniform within the stratum. It is found in clouds and patches of different densities. This is perhaps not so serious an obstacle when objects lying altogether outside the stratum are considered, because then the astronomer must necessarily look through the whole thickness. But for the hot stars of the Galaxy itself that lie within the stratum, the accidental occurrence of a very dense patch in the line of sight might produce an intense interstellar line in the spectrum of a star which is, astronomically speaking, close by. In the second place, the intensity of the interstellar lines must be calibrated with respect to distance. To do this the distances of a certain number of stars must be found independently of the interstellar line intensity criterion. Since the

stars must be remote from the sun in order to show the interstellar lines at all, their distances are hard to measure. The
trigonometric parallax method is hardly applicable and statistical parallaxes have in the main been used. The investigators themselves conclude that the distance of a star deduced
from the intensity of its interstellar lines 'should rarely be
more than 25 per cent in error' [3]. But other astronomers [4]
who wish to use their results, appear to be less enthusiastic
about the accuracy of the method.

Expanding Nebular Discs of Novae

A nova is a star which suddenly ejects a small fraction of its
material in the form of a cloud of gas, the brilliance of the
star and gas being enormously increased as compared with
the luminosity of the star before the outburst. The ejected gas
is seen as a luminous disc whose size increases with time. In
principle at least, this expanding cloud can be used to determine the distance of the nova. In fig. 5, *O* is the observer, *P* is

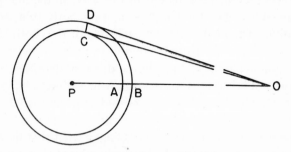

FIG. 5. Expanding shell of a nova.

the central star and *AC* and *BD* are portions of the outer edge
of the gas cloud at intervals of some years. The distance *AB*
may be calculated from the radial velocity which is deduced
from the displacement of the spectral lines of the luminous
gas as it travels from *A* to *B* along the line of sight *PO*. The

angle COD can also be determined by noting the enlargement of the disc during the time interval in question. If it is assumed that AB is equal to CD, Euclidean geometry will then give the distance of the star. The obstacles here are due to the asymmetric nature of nova explosions, the nebular discs rarely being of circular outline as we have assumed in fig. 5. Nor do the gases flow out at constant speeds and in a regular manner in all directions over a span of years. The result is that, of some 150 novae that have been observed in our Galaxy, scarcely ten have exploded in a sufficiently symmetrical manner for the method to be applied with some confidence. Their distances do not exceed 800 pc from the sun.

The Intensity of a Source of Radiation

A method of determining local distance, which is theoretically of universal application, depends on the properties of electromagnetic radiation. The radiation consists of electromagnetic waves, each wave being characterized by a wavelength λ and a frequency f that are related by $\lambda f = c$. The stream of waves of different wavelengths (or frequencies) emitted by a radiating source, carries energy with it. Suppose then that in each unit interval of frequency, called a cycle per second, the object emits energy impartially in all directions at a rate of $P(f)$ watts. If the observer is at a local distance of l metres from the source and is at rest with respect to it, this energy will be spread over the interior of a sphere of radius l when it reaches the observer. Thus on a square metre held by the observer at right angles to the stream of waves there will fall per second an amount of energy $P(f)/(4\pi l^2)$. It is this rate of arrival of energy per unit area which measures the intensity of the source as it appears to the observer. Clearly, this intensity varies as the inverse square of the local distance; doubling the distance reduces the intensity to one quarter of its previous value; trebling the distance means a reduction to one ninth, and so on. Thus, we might jump to the conclusion that the measurement of the intensity of a source would at once give the local distance, but this is unfortunately an illusion.

The arriving energy has first of all to be recorded, by the eye or the photographic plate or the photoelectric cell if its frequency corresponds to that of light waves and by a radio telescope if the frequency lies in the radio domain. No instrument is perfect and therefore only a part of the energy is actually measured, this fraction depending on the frequency. Thus the recorded energy will always be less than the actual energy arriving, $P(f)/(4\pi l^2)$. The factor by which it is reduced within the measuring instrument at each frequency f is known as the sensitivity function and is denoted by $\sigma(f)$. The recorded energy (S) is measured in watts (w) per cycle per second (c/s) per square metre (m), and we can therefore write the following formula:

$$S = \frac{\sigma(f)\,P(f)}{4\pi l^2} \text{ w (c/s)}^{-1}\text{ m}^{-2}\;.$$

This is the quantity found when using a radio telescope and is called in radio astronomy the flux-density of the source. The corresponding quantity when the source is an emitter of light will be discussed in a moment for it presents additional complications. Even if the sensitivity function $\sigma(f)$ were known, a measurement of S will not give l for the very good reason that the intrinsic power output $P(f)$ is unknown. However, this difficulty may be overcome when it is known that a number of sources are identical in power output, even if the value of the latter is undetermined. Because then P will be the same for all sources and so, incidentally, will be σ which is a property of the receiving apparatus. Thus if S_s and l_s are the flux-density and the local distance of the standard source, respectively, it follows that

$$\frac{l}{l_s} = \left(\frac{S_s}{S}\right)^{1/2}\;. \tag{3}$$

In this way the ratio of the distance of each source to that of the standard source could be found from the ratio of flux-densities.

In the optical domain, the principal additional factor arises from the fact that light-registering devices operate simultaneously over a range of frequency rather than at a single one. Thus the luminosity of a light source is the result of summing the flux-density over the range and this sum is equivalent to an integral. Hence the luminosity L is

$$L = \int S(f) \, df = \frac{1}{4\pi l^2} \int \sigma(f) \, P(f) \, df. \tag{4}$$

A further complication is introduced by the different sensitivities of the eye, the photographic plate and the photoelectric cell to light waves of different frequencies. This means that the sensitivity function is different for each type of device and this, of course, leads to different luminosities for one and the same object. However, within one category of luminosity the notion of a standard source gives rise to a formula corresponding to (3), namely,

$$\frac{l}{l_s} = \left(\frac{L_s}{L}\right)^{1/2}. \tag{5}$$

Ancient custom also dictates an alternative form for the last equation. In comparing the luminosity of one star with that of another it is convenient to speak of one star being so many times brighter than the next. Therefore instead of using the luminosity itself, a number called the *apparent magnitude* is employed. It has been internationally agreed that a star of apparent magnitude 6 shall be one whose luminosity is one hundredth of that of a star of apparent magnitude 1 and so on throughout the scale. It can then be proved that the luminosities L and L' of two stars whose apparent magnitudes are m and m', respectively, are related by the formula $L/L' = 100^{(m' - m)/5}$. It is easily seen that, if $m'=6$ and $m=1$, then

$L'=L/100$ in agreement with the international rule. Applying the formula to a source of luminosity L and to the standard source of luminosity L_s, we have

$$\frac{L_s}{L}=100^{\frac{1}{5}(m-m_s)}=10^{\frac{2}{5}(m-m_s)}, \tag{6}$$

and therefore

$$\log l-\log l_s=0\cdot2(m-m_s). \tag{7}$$

Another modification customary in optical astronomy concerns the identification of the standard source. In studying the stars of our Galaxy, the pre-supposition is that the local distance of a star and its apparent magnitude are measured independently of one another. The distance is thought of as something that is obtained from a trigonometric parallax, or by some alternative method that makes no use of luminosity criteria. In this way the intrinsic power output of the source can be determined from the inverse square law of brightness diminution. It is then possible to compute the apparent magnitude that the star would have if it were placed at the standard distance of 10 pc. This quantity is called the *absolute magnitude*, M, of the star. The star itself, placed in this fictitious position, is then taken as the standard source with which its actual apparent magnitude is to be compared. In fact, writing $l_s=10$ pc and $m_s=M$ in (7) it follows that

$$\log l=0\cdot2(m-M)+1. \tag{8}$$

The number $m-M$ for the star is called its *distance modulus*, because, once known, the local distance in parsecs is at once deduced from the formula.

This method of selecting the standard source is eminently suited to stellar astronomy; any star brought from its actual distance to 10 pc from the sun would still look like a star. It becomes somewhat artificial when used for an entire galaxy whose dimensions may run to tens of thousands of pc. What is meant by the absolute magnitude of a galaxy is the apparent magnitude of a single source of light, having stellar dimensions and equal in power output to the combined outputs of all luminous objects in the galaxy, when this fictitious object is placed at a distance of 10 pc from the sun. From the cosmological point of view, the absolute magnitude of a galaxy is an item of information which, combined with the observed apparent magnitude of the galaxy as a whole, will produce the distance modulus and therefore the local distance of the galaxy.

There is still an obstacle to be overcome before the local distance can be deduced from the distance modulus. The interstellar gas is mixed with dust which has a serious dimming effect on light traversing it [2]. The analogy is with a street lamp seen on a foggy day; the lamp looks dimmer and it also looks redder than it does when no fog is present. Astronomers have devised methods, largely based on the change of colour suffered by a star of known spectral type when its light traverses the obscuring clouds, which enable them to estimate what the apparent magnitude of the star would be were the obscuration absent. It is this apparent magnitude, corrected for absorption, that must be used in the distance modulus when calculating the distance. Happily, radio waves are almost unaffected by the obscuration and therefore radio flux-densities, when they are available, may be employed uncorrected in local distance determinations.

Finally it must be emphasized that the formulae given in this section do not enshrine eternal truths laid up in heaven to which no possible alternatives could be produced. Rather are they deductions from certain postulates such as the hypothesis of absolute Euclidean distance and absolute time of classical physics combined with the classical theory of the motion of radiation. They also pre-suppose, strictly speaking, that the observer and the source are at relative rest. In practice however, they can be regarded as valid if the relative speed of source and observer does not exceed 1,500 km/sec, a condition for the most part realized for objects inside our own Galaxy.

Galaxies with Local Distances

Amongst the hundreds or even thousands of millions of galaxies within the reach of the 200-inch telescope on Mount Palomar, there are a score or two which can be resolved into recognizably individual objects. The radial velocities of these few also indicate that their speeds relative to our Galaxy are less than 1,500 km/sec and therefore that the notion of local distance might be applicable, in an approximate fashion at least. It is indeed by a study of the resolvable galaxies, small as their number may be, that distances in the universe are ultimately established.

Neither trigonometric parallaxes nor statistical parallaxes are derivable for any galaxy and therefore all the direct methods of distance determination fail. It is perhaps possible that in the future measurements of the angular diameters of galaxies, whether in the optical or the radio domain, may yield distances. Encouraging results on optical diameters are being obtained by de Vaucouleurs [5]. At the present time, the distance of a galaxy usually means a distance determined by the luminosity criteria of the preceding section. The sequence of operations for a resolvable galaxy is, in principle, the following: firstly, a specific type of object is identified in the galaxy and the apparent magnitude of individual specimens is measured. The category of objects may be, for example, a class of variable stars or a group of novae, or the globular star clusters which the galaxy contains. Secondly, the absolute magnitude of the objects of the class is estimated by finding the distances to objects of similar type in our Galaxy. Thirdly, the obscuration between ourselves and the galaxy must be found. When all this has been done, the distance modulus of the object (or class of objects) in the galaxy is computed. But this must also be the distance modulus of the galaxy itself, since the objects in question are embedded in it. Clearly the procedure pre-supposes that the dimensions of the galaxy are small compared with its distance from our own and this is indeed found to be the case, even for the nearest galaxies.

An exhaustive description of the various classes of objects that have been employed to find the local distances of galaxies is beyond the scope of this book. We shall content ourselves with two only, the classical Cepheids and the novae. The former are variable stars whose luminosity rises and falls in a characteristic way, the period of an oscillation varying from star to star from somewhat over one day to about one hundred days. This type of variable star occurs in our own Galaxy and also in neighbouring ones, in particular, in the Small Magellanic Cloud. Fig. 6 shows the mean apparent

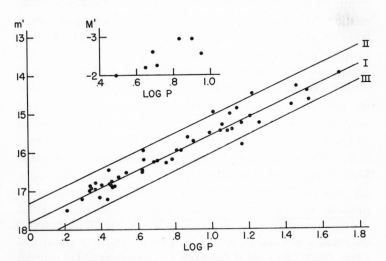

FIG. 6. Period-luminosity diagram for Cepheids in the Small Magellanic Cloud (after Arp) and for seven galactic Cepheids.

magnitude,* m', during a light fluctuation of forty-eight of these stars in the Small Magellanic Cloud plotted against the logarithm of their periods P in days [6]. Since all the stars of the Cloud are at approximately the same distance from the sun, the diagram shows that there must be a correlation between the mean *absolute* magnitude of the star and its period. Clearly, as the scatter of the points shows, the correlation is not unique; there is a certain latitude regarding the absolute magnitude which a star of given period can have. Indeed, recent theory [7] has shown that this is to be expected, the absolute magnitude depending not only on the period of the star but also on its colour. The straight line that passes evenly through the points in the diagram has the equation

$$m' = 17 \cdot 79 - 2 \cdot 25 \log P \qquad (9)$$

and it will be called the 'mean line' of this period-luminosity diagram. It is marked I in fig. 6 where the parallel lines II and III are also shown. These two enclose all but three of the points and they lie one magnitude apart. It is perhaps pessimistic to conclude that the spread in absolute magnitude for stars of given period is as large as this, but it is best to be cautious in this respect.

Before proceeding with the determination of the absolute magnitudes that correspond to the apparent magnitudes in the diagram, it is worth noting that the diagram itself could be used to determine the *relative* distances of all galaxies in which a sufficient number of classical Cepheids were detectable. If the apparent magnitudes were measured on the same system, each galaxy would have its own period-luminosity diagram. Assuming that the Cepheids in all galaxies behave in the same way, the mean lines in all these diagrams would

* Here m' stands for a B magnitude on the (B, V) system. This magnitude system depends on measuring the amount of electromagnetic energy received from the star in light of various colours. The B stands for the measurement made mainly in blue light, the V for one mainly in yellow light.

have the same slope, indicating the same constant correlation between magnitude and period for all galaxies. Superposing this diagram on that of the Small Magellanic Cloud so that the periods corresponded would give at once the difference of the distance moduli of the two galaxies.* This expectation is based on the assumption that classical Cepheids in all galaxies are sufficiently similar for the mean lines in their period-luminosity diagrams to have the same slope. But if the classical Cepheids did not, in fact, possess this property, the superposition of diagrams would reveal it, in itself an interesting item of information. It is to be hoped that observational investigations of this kind will in future be carried out, in spite of their laborious and time-consuming nature.

Meanwhile one may attempt to find the distance of the Small Magellanic Cloud in parsecs. The ideal would be to find the distances of many galactic Cepheids of different periods, evaluate the absolute magnitude of each from its known distance and measured apparent magnitude and then construct a period-luminosity diagram for the Galaxy. This would show absolute magnitude plotted against the logarithm of the period. The small upper diagram in fig. 6 is a rudimentary diagram of this kind [8]. The points for seven Cepheids of our Galaxy that occur in galactic clusters of known distance are indicated. Superposing this diagram on that for the Small Magellanic Cloud, the best fit is obtained if the line $M' = -2$ in the small diagram falls on

---

* The mean line for the period-luminosity diagram of the galaxy would be

$$m' = g - 2 \cdot 25 \log P$$

where g is some constant and the factor $2 \cdot 25$ corresponds to the constant slope of the mean line mentioned above. Thus treating the Small Magellanic Cloud as the standard source and using (7) and (9) there comes

$$\log (l/l_s) = (g - 17 \cdot 79)/5.$$

where l is the distance of the galaxy and l_s that of the Small Magellanic Cloud.

$m'=16.6$ in the large one. This means that the distance modulus of the Small Cloud is 18·6 and the relation between absolute magnitude and $\log P$ is

$$M' = -0.82 - 2.25 \log P$$

But the calibration of the two diagrams is weak because the seven galactic Cepheids have so small a range in $\log P$. Another method of calibration makes use of the statistical parallax of a group of 17 classical Cepheids in our Galaxy [9]. The proper motions and obscurations of these stars are sufficiently well known to give a statistical parallax of some reliability. The average distance of the group turns out to be 307 pc. and the average *photographic* apparent magnitude of the 17 stars, corrected for obscuration, is $m=4.43$. Their average period corresponds to $\log P=0.761$. Now an object at 307 pc whose apparent magnitude is 4·43 must have an absolute magnitude of $M=-3.01$, and this presumably corresponds to $\log P=0.761$. Again, from the mean line of fig. 6, $\log P=0.761$ gives $m'=16.18$ and this converts to photographic magnitude $m=16.08$. Therefore the distance modulus of the Small Magellanic Cloud is

$$m-M=16.08+3.01 \simeq 19.1$$

which corresponds to a distance of 66,000 pc or about 215,000 ly. Though a distance has thus been obtained, its reliability cannot be high if for no other reason than that a statistical method of distance determination applied to a population of 17 is unlikely to arouse much confidence. Nevertheless, astronomers are inclined to believe that a distance modulus for the Small Magellanic Cloud of 19, or a little more, is in better agreement with all available lines of evidence than is one as low as 18·6.

Cosmologically speaking, the actual distance of a nearby galaxy is less interesting than the absolute magnitude of the galaxy as a whole. Since the apparent photographic magnitude of the Small Magellanic Cloud is $m=2\cdot59$ its absolute magnitude is $M=-19\cdot1+2\cdot6=-16\cdot5$. A corresponding calculation, which will not be given here in detail, for the Large Magellanic Cloud suggests that its absolute magnitude is $-18\cdot4$ or $-18\cdot5$, with about the same degree of reliability as for the Small Magellanic Cloud. Proceeding further afield, the great galaxy Messier 31 (M 31) seen through the stars in the constellation Andromeda also contains many classical Cepheids. The observers have published few details of their investigations but it is stated that the distance modulus is $24\cdot25$. Since the apparent magnitude of the galaxy is $4\cdot33$, it follows that its absolute magnitude is -19.92. The distance is uncertain because, unlike the case of the Magellanic

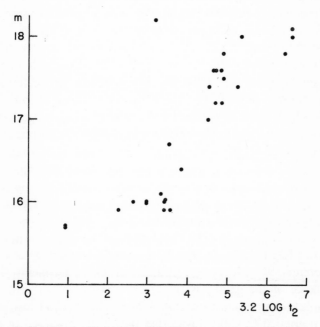

FIG. 7. Brightness diminution diagram for novae in the Andromeda Galaxy (M 31).

Clouds, there is thought to be an appreciable obscuration between us and M 31. Opinions as to the amount of the obscuration vary and therefore the distance probably lies between 450,000 and 525,000 pc and so is of the order of $1\frac{1}{2}$ million light-years.

The Cepheid variables as distance indicators tend to give distances which are on the small side. At the other extreme, the novae indicate larger distances for the same galaxies. The property employed is a relationship that appears to exist between the absolute magnitude of a nova at maximum light and its subsequent rate of fading. This effect is shown in fig. 7 for 28 novae [10] in the galaxy M 31. The apparent magnitude of each nova at maximum has been plotted against the quantity $3 \cdot 2 \log t_2$, where t_2 is the time in days which is needed for the nova to fall two magnitudes from maximum. Since all these novae are at approximately the same distance, it is clear that novae which are intrinsically bright at maximum fade more rapidly than those—at the right-hand side of the diagram—which are relatively less luminous at maximum. Now, in our own Galaxy, there are eleven novae whose distances have been determined and whose absolute magnitudes at maximum can therefore be computed from the corresponding observed apparent magnitudes. Fig. 8 shows the diagram for these eleven [11], where t_2 has the same meaning as in fig. 7. If the diagrams are superposed so that the values of $3 \cdot 2 \log t_2$ fit on one another, it turns out that the best identification is obtained when $m = 15 \cdot 6$ of fig. 7 lies on $M = -9$ of fig. 8. From this it may be concluded that the distance modulus of M 31 is $15 \cdot 6 - (-9) = 24 \cdot 6$, which is an increase of $0 \cdot 35$ as compared with the one obtained from the Cepheids. The distance of the galaxy is thus increased by 18 per cent, its absolute magnitude to about $-20 \cdot 3$. The method has also been applied to eight novae that have been observed in the Small Magellanic Cloud and in this case the increase of

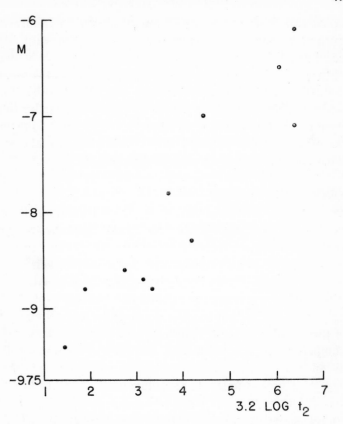

FIG. 8. Brightness diminution diagram for eleven galactic novae.

distance modulus is from 19·1 to 19·2, extending the distance by some 5 per cent.

At first sight the nova method appears to provide the answer to the distance problem and it was so greeted by many astronomers when it was first published by Schmidt in 1957 [11]. Further reflection however shows that it shares a defect with the classical Cepheid method, namely, there are too few comparison objects in our own Galaxy. The eleven

D

novae constitute a very small group of objects for calibration purposes, even if their distances were known with high accuracy. This is in itself an optimistic conclusion: only seven of the eleven have their distances determined from the rate of expansion of their shells of ejected gas, for the other four indirect methods such as the intensities of interstellar lines must be used. It would seem wiser for the moment to regard the method as one amongst others, rather than to take it as the touchstone for all distance determinations.

Absolute Magnitudes of Galaxies

The distances of those galaxies in which individual objects can be separately identified by the largest telescopes are important not only in themselves but also because, as we have seen, they give a clue to the intrinsic luminosity of each galaxy taken as a whole. These absolute magnitudes of galaxies constitute important cosmological data because they provide the only distance criterion which is available for the vast majority of these stellar systems. Apart, indeed, from that very small number which are resolvable, the only indication of the distance of a galaxy lies in its apparent magnitude and this in its turn is useless unless the absolute magnitude can be estimated. During the year which ended in July 1956, the present author carried out a survey of the literature on distances in the realm of the galaxies and concluded that there was reason to believe that the absolute magnitudes of the intrinsically brightest galaxies lay in the range −18·9 and −19·9 of absolute magnitude [12]. Since that time additional information has become available in the nova method of distance determination which has been described above and also in the work of Holmberg [13] who has studied the surface-brightness of some 300 bright spiral galaxies. On the whole it would appear that the absolute magnitudes of the most luminous galaxies were underestimated in 1956 and that a better range is probably −19·9 to −20·9. We shall tentatively adopt these figures and use them when we come later on to estimate the rate of expansion of the universe. It cannot however be too strongly emphasized that the whole subject of distance determinations, as it refers to galaxies, is a rapidly developing one and that certainty is as yet very far from having been reached.

Chapter 3

THE SYSTEM OF GALAXIES

In this chapter we shall describe the types of observational data which, in addition to the distance of galaxies, are essential to cosmology. A fundamental observation concerns the character of the distribution in space of these objects, the way in which they lie with respect to one another and to our own Galaxy. The second fundamental datum concerns the displacement of the spectral lines in the spectra of galaxies, the so-called red-shift, by which each line is moved towards the red end of the spectrum compared with that of a laboratory source. And a third item of importance depends on the interaction between this red-shift and the manner in which the galaxy emits radiation at different frequencies.

Spatial Distribution of Galaxies

A photograph of long exposure taken with a powerful telescope reveals the images of large numbers of galaxies in each square degree of the sky. These images are of different apparent magnitudes but as a general rule their number increases the fainter the galaxies appear to be. Even a casual inspection of the photographs of the Sky Atlas* reveals that the number of galaxies per square degree is very variable. Indeed in a

* The National Geographic Society – Palomar Observatory Sky Atlas made with the 48-inch Schmidt telescope on Mount Palomar. It covers the whole sky north of declination −27°. Two photographs of each region of the sky are provided, one taken in blue light, the other in red. The limiting photographic magnitude of the blue plates is 21·1 and, of the red, 20·0.

band some 20 to 25 degrees wide through the centre of which runs the plane of our Galaxy, hardly any are seen. This effect is interpreted as an accident due to the location of the sun near that plane, which also contains the bulk of the obscuring matter in our Galaxy. The 'zone of avoidance' is thus a local effect and not a gap in the distribution of galaxies. Elsewhere it is possible to say that, though the number of galaxies per unit area of the sky does vary,* there are no preferred directions producing over-all excesses or defects of galaxies. It does appear therefore that the arrangement of the galaxies in space, whatever it may be in detail, is isotropic with respect to our own provided, of course, that the celestial photographs are of such a kind as to reveal galaxies which are sufficiently faint. By isotropic is meant that the distribution is the same in whatever direction we look.

But when the photographs are examined unit area by unit area, it is obvious that the galaxy images exhibit a marked tendency to 'clumpiness'. Since each photograph records in superposition all galaxies bright enough to make an impression on the plate, it might be thought that statistical fluctuations would account for this phenomenon. However, it was noted as long ago as the 1920s that there were groupings of galaxy images here and there in the sky which were relatively compact. They were interpreted as the images of clusters of galaxies whose constituent members formed physical systems that were not accidental groupings. It was first thought that these conspicuous clusters, which are after all not very numerous compared with the total number of galaxies, were concentrations occurring sporadically in a uniform distribution of 'field galaxies'. But the work of Zwicky [15] at Mount

* Counts of 20 to 60 galaxies per square degree are common in the Lick survey [14] to the 18th magnitude. Regions of up to 300 galaxies per square degree also occur. Since there are 41,253 square degrees in the entire sky, the reader can estimate for himself the immense number of galaxies with images no fainter than the 18th magnitude.

Wilson and Palomar, of Shane [14] and his collaborators at Lick, and the statistical investigations of Neyman and Scott [16] at Berkeley have led to a modification of these ideas. It would seem that the distribution of galaxy images on a plate of long exposure made with a powerful telescope is statistically different from a random one. The conclusion is that the tendency of galaxies to occur in clusters is a very wide-spread one and that there may well be no such thing as a background 'field' of galaxies in which the large clusters are embedded. Ignoring for the moment this question of clustering, we ask how the increase in numbers of galaxy images with increasing apparent magnitude could be used to discover how the galaxies are distributed in space.

A little theory will help to answer this question. Consider a universe filled with galaxies at rest with respect to one another, each galaxy being intrinsically as luminous as any other. Suppose also that this universe is that of classical physics, with its absolute distance and time, its Euclidean geometry and its classical theory of the motion of radiation. If the galaxies are scattered uniformly in such a universe, their number per unit volume, or their *number-density*, will be some constant n. The total number of galaxies within a sphere of outer radius l is then easily calculated to be $N = 4\pi n l^3/3$. The luminosity of every galaxy being, by hypothesis, equal to the same quantity L, it follows from equation (4) of Chapter 2 that L is proportional to l^{-2}. But by equation (7) of Chapter 2, it also follows that $\log l = 0 \cdot 2m + constant$, where m is the apparent magnitude of a galaxy distant l. Hence it follows that the total number of galaxies counted by an observer located at the centre of the sphere that have apparent magnitudes not fainter than m, is

$$\log N = 0 \cdot 6m + constant. \tag{1}$$

If the galaxies are emitters of radio waves of equal power output, the corresponding formula obtained by combining N proportional to l^3 with equation (3) of Chapter 2 is

$$N = (constant)\ S^{-3/2}, \qquad (2)$$

the count including all galaxies whose flux-densities are observed to be not less than S. In radio astronomy, the second formula has come to be known as the 'minus three-halves' law. Both formulae are often referred to in the literature as if they were immutable laws, defining the concept of 'uniformity of distribution'. They are in fact valid only if all the postulates of classical physics are accepted, and if moreover it is assumed that all galaxies are of equal output of radiation and are also at mutual relative rest. Though much of cosmology consists in escaping from these classical chains, they may for the moment be accepted in order to see where they lead us as tools for interpreting the observations.

We discuss here the situation as it appears when galaxies are regarded as optical sources. It might seem easy at first sight to test whether the number of galaxies counted over a given (large) area of the sky did, or did not, follow the rule (1). With the same powerful telescope, the given area would be successively photographed with exposure times of increasing duration. Since a long exposure time permits the recording of fainter objects than does a short one, each successive plate would have a 'limiting magnitude' fainter than the preceding one. Thus, counting the number of galaxies recorded for each plate of successively greater exposure time would give the number N for a sequence of values of m. It would then be simple to check whether or not the pairs of number (N, m) fitted the rule (1). This, in principle, was the method used by the astronomers of the 1930s, notably Hubble [17], and they concluded that the distribution of galaxies in space was uniform in the sense of equation (1), provided that the limiting magnitude was not too faint. By this Hubble meant that, if m were pushed to 19 and onwards to 21, then the data appeared to fit better the rule

$$\log N = 0.501m + constant, \tag{3}$$

a formula which it will be convenient to write as

$$\log N = (0.6 + \mu/5)m + constant, \tag{4}$$

where μ is sufficiently accurately taken to be the *negative* number -0.5.

The subsequent history of these investigations has been a curious one. It is easy to allow for the fact that all galaxies are not of equal intrinsic luminosity provided that it can be assumed that there is a 'most frequent' luminosity. But it very soon became evident that the determination of the apparent magnitude of a galaxy was a much more difficult problem than for a star, which looks like a point source of light even in the largest of telescopes. This was particularly true when the limiting magnitude of the plate was in question. The limiting magnitude for different types of galaxies was not the same; it differed from one part of a plate to another and it also varied from plate to plate [14]. Thus in each (N, m) pair, the value of m is subject to large and uncertain errors. But even if this could be overcome another disagreeable feature of the operation emerged: the process of counting the images of galaxies is a fatiguing and laborious one and the result is that counts by the same investigator on the same plate carried out at two different times may differ widely in amount. Thus both N and m are uncertain and the agreement with either (1) or (3) loses its cogency. If this were not bad enough, the recognition of the universality of the phenomenon of clustering throws much doubt on the validity of the notion that there is an average number of galaxies per unit area of the sky. Without such a concept, it has been argued by one investigator at least [18], there is no justification for using (1) at all. This is perhaps an extreme view, because it seems to be clear that, if the unit area of the sky is taken to be large enough, an average number per unit area is applicable. Thus in the work of Shane, it does appear that the effect of clustering ceases to be important when the unit area is larger than 4 degrees by the side.

Astronomers have thus apparently discredited most of the evidence on which the uniformity of distribution in space of the galaxies had been based. Stated in mathematical terms, the empirical value of μ in equation (4) would seem to be undetermined and there is therefore presumably no reason for supposing that it is zero, the value it must take if equation (4) is to reduce to equation (1), and thus give constant distribution in the universe of classical physics. If this is really so, it seems odd that the notion of the uniformity of distribution of galaxies in space should persist as strongly as it does. Possibly the attitude of the observers has been misinterpreted: it may be that they rely on a general qualitative impression obtained from photographs of the same region of the sky taken with telescopes of increasing power and increasing exposure times. Or perhaps there is a tacit unacknowledged agreement that counts extending to the 15th or 16th magnitude are indeed good enough to test the hypothesis (1), but that Hubble's attempt to push the counts down to the 21st magnitude and to draw far-reaching cosmological conclusions from a non-zero value of μ in (4) are now regarded as objectionable. Whatever the reason, there seems to be agreement that the over-all distribution of galaxies in space is roughly uniform in the classical sense, with the qualification that the unit of volume must be large enough.*

Clusters of Galaxies

The number of galaxies that form a cluster is very variable [15]. An example of a small cluster is the Local Group, with some 24 members, a cluster to which our Galaxy, M 31

---

* Oort [19] considers that the diameter of a unit volume must be not less than about 350 megaparsec. He employs a distance scale such that the distance of the Virgo cluster is 15 megaparsec.

and the Magellanic Clouds belong. At the other extreme are to be found clusters like the Coma cluster, which perhaps contain 100,000 galaxies. A definition of a cluster has been given by Abell [20] in his study of the clusters that are registered on the red plates of the Sky Atlas. The distance of the cluster must first be estimated and this is done by assuming that the tenth brightest galaxy of every cluster has the same intrinsic luminosity. A grouping of galaxies, in order to qualify as a cluster, must contain at least 50 members that are not more than 2 magnitudes fainter than the third brightest member, and they must lie within a certain distance of the centre of the agglomeration. Some 2,712 clusters of this kind were found. If the number of clusters is counted for each successive step in m – the apparent magnitude of the tenth brightest cluster member – then the distribution of clusters does follow roughly the rule (1). Thus whatever may be the case for individual galaxies, it can be argued that clusters are distributed uniformly in the classical sense.

An important observational datum connected with clusters refers to the way in which the members of a cluster can be ranked according to their apparent magnitudes. Since all the cluster members are approximately equidistant from the terrestrial observer, the differences of apparent magnitude reflect differences in absolute magnitude. Some pioneer work in this direction has been done by Sandage [21] who studied 18 clusters. He found that the differences between the apparent magnitudes of the first, third, fifth and tenth brightest cluster members were roughly constant from cluster to cluster. Indeed, it was possible to define a *synthetic brightest member* for each cluster by using the average differences of magnitude between these four cluster-members in each system. Investigations of this kind should help to throw light on the vexed question of whether or not the brightest members of each cluster are of approximately the same intrinsic luminosity. If this is the case, then Sandage's result presents no problem. But if the brightest galaxies in the various clusters have systematically different luminosities, it is at least peculiar that the luminosities of the first few members of each cluster should bear constant ratios to each other.

A crude idea of the distances of clusters may be obtained by the use of equation (8) of Chapter 2, which implies that local (Euclidean) distance is applicable and that a cluster and the observer on earth have no appreciable relative motion. The nearest of the great clusters is the Virgo cluster; a relatively distant one is the Hydra cluster (0855 +0321). The synthetic brightest galaxies of the two clusters have apparent magnitudes of 9·17 and 18·78, respectively. On the assumption that the corresponding absolute magnitude lies in the range −19.9 to −20.9, the local distance of the Virgo cluster has some value in the interval 6·5 to 10·3 megaparsec. The corresponding interval for the Hydra cluster is 540 to 860 megaparsec. Though distances calculated in this fashion are frequently quoted, especially in connection with the range of the 200-inch Mount Palomar telescope, it will be shown in later chapters of this book that they must be taken with a substantial grain of salt.

Class II Radio Sources

The investigations made with radio telescopes have shown that sources of radio waves in the astronomical universe may be classified into two main categories: Class I sources which are associated with our Galaxy and Class II sources that are outside it. The latter have small angular diameters and are distributed isotropically around our Galaxy. That most, if not all, of the Class II sources are galaxies seems to be highly probable, though it must be confessed that the identification of such a source with an optical object is surprisingly difficult. For example, the catalogue made by Mills and his colleagues [22] at Sydney, Australia, contains some one thousand of these sources; yet the number of optical identifications remains very small [23]. But the results are remarkable for they show that these identified sources are galaxies of peculiar kinds. Sometimes they are objects interpreted as pairs of galaxies in collision (Cygnus A, NGC 1275), or they are elliptical galaxies with two or more centres, or, as in the case of NGC 4486, the galaxy contains the unusual feature of a jet of gas apparently being ejected from its central region. Catalogues such as the Australian also contain the flux-density of each source at the frequency of operation of the radio telescope, and therefore it is possible to count the number N of sources having flux-densities greater than or equal to S. For Mills's catalogue the empirical relation between N and S turns out to be

$$N = (constant)\ S^{-(3+\mu)/2}, \quad \mu = 0 \cdot 3. \qquad (5)$$

Here μ has exactly the same significance as it had in Hubble's formula (4), but its value turns out to be *positive*. Thus whereas Hubble thought he had established a defect in the number of galaxies, as compared with the prediction of the classical formula (1), the Mills survey suggests that there is an excess of Class II sources as compared with the (equivalent) criterion (2). The range of flux-density is from 160×10^{-26} watts per sq. metre per cycle per second to 7×10^{-26} wm^{-2}(c/s)$^{-1}$. A similar type of survey [24] has been made by the workers in Cambridge, England, and μ has been found to be equal to unity.

It may be that the difficulty of optical identifications and the strange distribution law (5) are merely due to instrumental defects. A radio telescope does not fix the position of a source of radiation with the pin-point accuracy that an optical telescope achieves. The radio source is fixed as lying within an area of the sky which is large from the optical point of view. Two or more radio sources close together in this region might therefore well be counted as a single one. Moreover a radio telescope 'looks' in more than one direction at a time, feebly in the direction of its side lobes and strongly in that of its main lobe. Hence a strong source in a side lobe might be erroneously counted as a weak source in the direction of the main lobe. Thus the difficulty of optical identifications might simply be due to the inaccuracy of position for all but the strongest radio sources and the distribution law (5) might arise because too many spurious weak sources have been included in the catalogue. But this is a very pessimistic view, because when identifications *are* made, the optical objects are relatively inconspicuous on the Sky Atlas. The most powerful of the Class II sources, Cygnus A, is indeed so very unnoticeable that it was overlooked until the radio astronomers drew attention to the region in which it lay. Thus we are led to suspect that the catalogues are perhaps better than they are thought to be and that the Class II radio sources are galaxies which are extremely remote and so optically very inconspicuous. If this is so, then their study would well repay attention and, in particular, we should have no reason to believe that their distribution in space need follow the classical rule (2).

The Red-shift

The spectrum of an entire galaxy can be photographed and it shows the usual succession of dark lines – the spectral lines – against an illuminated background. The sequences of lines due to some of the simpler chemical elements are identifiable; in particular, the H and K lines of the element calcium are usually conspicuous. When the spectra of large numbers of galaxies are studied, a remarkable statistical effect is noticed. The larger the number which expresses the apparent magnitude of the galaxy, the more its spectral lines are displaced towards the red, or longer wavelength, end of the spectrum.

This displacement is, of course, relative to a laboratory source on earth and it is known as the red-shift.

A first step toward the interpretation of the phenomenon involves the determination of the way in which the different lines in the spectrum of a given galaxy are displaced. If λ is the laboratory wavelength of a line and $\lambda + d\lambda$ is the wavelength as measured in the galaxy spectrum, then a convenient measure of the red-shift for the line is

$$\delta = d\lambda/\lambda, \tag{6}$$

as in the case of stellar spectra. The critical question is: does δ vary from line to line in a given galaxy spectrum, or does it remain constant? Only three or four galaxies have been studied from this point of view, the most careful investigation being that of Minkowski and O. C. Wilson [25] on the spectrum of Cygnus A. Ten lines were measured, five in the violet-blue region and five in the red, these lines thus having wavelengths in the range from about $3,400 \times 10^{-8}$ cm. to $6,600 \times 10^{-8}$ cm. The displacement of each line was measured independently by each observer on more than one plate. The average δ thus obtained for each line is plotted in fig. 9. The circled point corresponds to a line which was found difficult

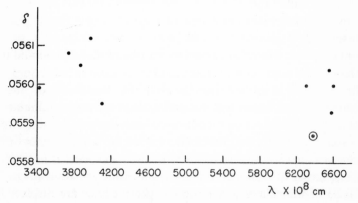

FIG. 9. Spectral line displacements (red-shift) for Cygnus A.

to measure and the observers consider that it should probably be disregarded.

The diagram suggests that δ is slightly smaller in the red region, on the right of the figure, than it is in the violet-blue. But this impression is mainly due to the presence of the circled point. If this is ignored, and the errors in the determinations are carefully considered, it turns out that the average δ for the five violet-blue lines is 0.05604 ± 0.00003 whereas it is 0.05599 ± 0.00002 for the four lines in the red. In each case mean errors have been quoted. Hence δ is indeed constant throughout the spectrum and its value is 0.05602. These slight systematic variations of δ across the spectrum of a galaxy occur in other cases also; for example, O. C. Wilson [26] found a slight increase of δ with wavelength for the case of NGC 4151, in contrast to the apparent decrease for Cygnus A. But such variations are insignificant though their origin has not been explained. No shred of doubt would remain as to the constancy of δ in the spectrum of a galaxy if the red-shift could be measured at radio wavelengths as well as at optical. In the radio domain there is one spectral line, that of neutral hydrogen, which has a wavelength of 21 cm. In 1956, Lilley and McClain believed that they had observed this line in the radio emission of Cygnus A and that it was displaced in accordance with the average red-shift of the optical lines. However, attempts to repeat the observations three years later showed that the identification of the 21 cm. line was due to an instrumental error and that this line, displaced or not, was in fact unobservable in the radio emission of Cygnus A.

Accepting then the constancy of δ for the spectral lines of any one galaxy, we need an explanation of the phenomenon. Displacements of spectral lines in the spectra of stars in our Galaxy are, of course, well known. They occur either towards the red or towards the violet end of the spectrum and they rarely exceed $\delta=0.001$ in magnitude. Such displacements are unhesitatingly interpreted by astronomers as the effects of relative velocity of star and observer, and they give the radial velocities which help to determine the distances of objects in our Galaxy. But in the case of the galaxies, the phenomenon presents a number of new features. Statistically speaking, it is an overwhelmingly one-way effect. All displacements are towards the red, except for a few very bright and therefore presumably nearby galaxies. Again, it assumes enormous proportions; photographically measured red-shifts have now reached $\delta=0.4614$ and correspondingly large values have also been independently found by photoelectric techniques, as can be seen from Table C of the Appendix. A red-shift of 0.46, interpreted by the classical Doppler formula (2) of Chapter 2, would represent a velocity of recession of 138,000 km/sec, which is a large fraction of the velocity of light. And lastly there appears to be a correlation between the average apparent magnitude of a galaxy and its red-shift of such a kind that an increase in the former corresponds to an increase in the latter also. Since apparent magnitude is a rough index of the distance of the galaxy, it would seem that the more distant a galaxy, the larger is its velocity of recession. Though, as will be shown presently, the correlation between red-shift and distance is not one of simple proportionality, it is nevertheless true that increase of distance does imply increase of the recessional velocity. It should also be noticed that the red-shift is isotropic with respect to our Galaxy; in other words, red-shifts of galaxies of the same apparent magnitude are the same in whatever direction the galaxies lie.

The qualitative picture suggested by these observations is that of a system of galaxies expanding as if from some point near our Galaxy. The velocity of recession is the greater the further away the galaxy lies and the motion of expansion is isotropic. The magnitude of the red-shift appears to be limited rather by our methods of observation than by anything else. If spectra of excessively faint galaxies could be measured, there seems to be no reason why red-shifts greater than 0·46 should not be observed.

It must be emphasized that it is the red-shift phenomenon which is responsible for the notion of an expanding universe of galaxies. These objects, in fact, show no other obvious evidence of being in relative motion: their relative positions do not change, nor do their angular diameters alter as time goes on. Moreover the interpretation of the red-shift as an effect of velocity depends on the constancy of this quantity for all lines in a given galactic spectrum. Attempts at interpretations other than this have not been lacking. For example, it has been argued that the galaxies are at relative rest but that the light they emit has been altered during its journey through space. There might be particles in this intervening space with which the light waves would collide. Their wavelength would be lengthened and the waves would be scattered as well. But the result of such repeated collisions would not be to alter the wavelength in the manner observed. And it is doubtful if the scattering would in any case permit us to photograph a remote galaxy at all. Alternatively, it can be imagined that light waves interacted in some hitherto unsuspected fashion with one another. The interaction can be adjusted to give the observed red-shift but then, if light did behave in this way, there would be striking effects in eclipsing binary stars. These are not observed. Finally, an appeal can be made to a result of general relativity which shows that a red-shift can be produced by intense gravitational fields. But then it would be necessary to assume that our Galaxy lay in a gravitational hole in the universe and that, as we receded from our Galaxy, more and more intense gravitational fields would be encountered. Such a notion merely replaces one mystery by another. In short, it is possible to imagine inter-

E

pretations of the red-shift that do not involve the concept of relative velocity, but as soon as one of these proposals is examined in detail, it is found to entail either contradictions with observation, or consequences which are inexplicable. Thus it may be concluded that the only satisfactory interpretation of the red-shift is in terms of relative velocity.*

The enormous relative velocities implied by the red-shifts that are observed have an important consequence. It will be remembered that the theory of local distance, which led to such formulae as (3), (5) and (8) of Chapter 2, took it for granted that the relative velocity of source and observer was small compared with that of light. The same is true of the classical Doppler formula (2) of Chapter 2 and of the distribution in space formulae (1) and (2) of the present chapter. Thus the red-shift kicks away one of the principal props under the classical theories which are so comfortably familiar to astronomers. It will be necessary to re-formulate these ideas and to think through again from first principles the concepts of distance, of relative velocity, and of the uniformity of distribution in space for the galaxies.

Spectral Energy-Curves

The sources of radiation found in nature emit energy – in the form of electromagnetic waves – of different amounts at different frequencies. This has already been noted in the calculation of the luminosity of an optical source through the presence of the function P of equation (4), Chapter 2, which depends on the frequency. It has proved possible to measure the energy emitted at different wavelengths (or at the equivalent frequencies) by certain galaxies. In fig. 10, the spectral energy-curve I represents the measurements made by Steb-

* See the second item of Reference [16] for a statement that the velocity interpretation requires 'verification'. No alternative physical process for the production of the red-shift is, however, suggested.

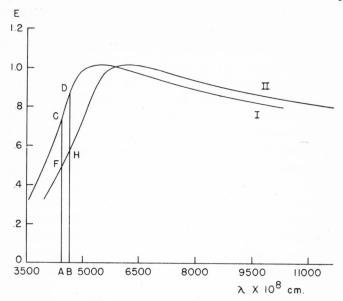

FIG. 10. Spectral energy-curves. Curve I is the observed curve for the Galaxy M 32. Curve II is Curve I displaced for a red-shift of 0.13.

bins and Whitford [27] on the elliptical nebula M 32, which is a companion of M 31. The units of energy, E, are relative ones, and give the ratio of the energy emitted at each frequency as a fraction of the average energy measured by the apparatus in the blue, green and red. The curve shows that the energy emitted increases rapidly with wavelength from about $\lambda = 3,500 \times 10^{-8}$ cm. to $5,500 \times 10^{-8}$ cm., and then falls off very much more slowly. Now suppose that there is a second source which is intrinsically similar to M 32, but is remote and therefore exhibits a red-shift of amount δ. Then the energy radiated at wavelength λ reaches the observer with wavelength $\lambda (1 + \delta)$. The principal effect on the spectral energy-curve is to displace the measured points parallel to the λ-axis so that they now fall at the wavelength $\lambda(1 + \delta)$.

Curve II shows the effect of this distortion for a source having red-shift 0·13. The skewing of the spectral energy-curve results in a change in the luminosity assigned to the source with a red-shift as compared with that of M 32. For the sake of argument, suppose that the photographic plate employed to register the incoming energy is sensitive to light in the band 4,300 to $4,500 \times 10^{-8}$ cm. Then the 'relative' apparent magnitude of M 32 would be proportional to the area $ABCD$. But for the source with red-shift 0·13, the corresponding apparent magnitude would be proportional to the smaller area $ABFH$. Therefore the apparent magnitude of the second source would be underestimated because of the red-shift, quite apart from the decrease of luminosity due to its greater distance. It is therefore to be expected that a correction to the apparent magnitude of a galaxy depending on its red-shift will have to be made in order that all galaxies should have their apparent magnitudes measured on the same system. This K-correction, as it is called, will be dealt with in more detail later in this book.

The Class II radio sources have, it is believed, much simpler spectral energy-curves than do optical sources. The emission of energy follows the rule that the flux-density is proportional to (frequency)^x. The number x is called the spectral index and its value is not yet known with certainty [28]. Radio sources of Class I, which are in our own Galaxy, probably have spectral indices equal to -0.6, whereas the brighter Class II sources have $x = -0.8$, and the fainter ones $x = -1.3$. Since the position is not quite clear at the time of writing, it will be assumed that for Class II sources, x may have any value in the range -0.75 to -1.2.

The (frequency)^x rule has been traced from 30 to 10,000 Mc/s, which means from a wavelength of 10 metres to one of 3 cm. Incidentally this shows how very extensive the radio spectrum is compared with the optical one. In fig. 10 there is little more than a threefold increase of wavelength across the diagram. On the other hand the interval from 3 cm. to 10 cm. corresponds to a factor of more than 330 between the two extreme wavelengths.

Chapter 4

THEORIES OF COSMOLOGY

The preceding two chapters have contained a description of the phenomena which are relevant to cosmology; it is now necessary to turn to the theoretical interpretation of these data by which they are welded into a coherent whole. The theories that have been employed have included the classical mechanics of Newton but, for the most part, investigators have tended to use one or other of the theories of relativity. It is to a general description of these disciplines that we now proceed.

Why Relativity?

In cosmology, as in other branches of science, it is almost impossible to describe the phenomena without at the same time making use of some theory. The reader will have noticed that this was done in the last two chapters and that, whenever necessary, classical physics was drawn upon. Since these theories are familiar to most people interested in science, it is tempting to argue that classical concepts should alone be used in cosmology. But two awkward facts militate against the adoption of this line of least resistance. The first of these is that when the red-shift is interpreted as an effect of velocity, the resulting velocities are large fractions of the velocity of light. It has been known for nearly sixty years that classical mechanics breaks down under these circumstances and that Einstein's special theory of relativity is the appropriate theoretical tool to use when high velocities are in question.

The second awkward fact concerns the question of gravitation, that force which appears to be the dominant one when bodies of large mass influence one another's motion. When intense gravitational fields have to be considered, it is known that Newton's theory of gravitation has to be replaced by Einstein's theory of general relativity. Even in the solar system the motion of the planet Mercury is more accurately described by the latter than by the former. It may be, of course, that the gravitational field of all the material content of the universe is a weak one; but, if true, this must be demonstrated and not assumed at the beginning of the inquiry. The conclusion is that, to make sure that the effects of high velocities and of (possibly) intense gravitational fields are properly accounted for, some form of relativity theory must be used. In considering theories of this kind, we shall begin with the two that are associated with the name of Einstein [29].

Special Relativity

It is well-known that special relativity owed a good part of its origin to the Michelson-Morley experiment, which was intended to measure the speed of the Earth in its orbit by a purely optical experiment performed in a laboratory from which no astronomical object was visible. The expectation of success depended on calculations based on the principles of the Newtonian theory of motion applied both to the motion of the Earth and to that of light. The experiment revealed that the expectation was unjustified – that the Earth's orbital speed could not be measured in this way and that failure was not due to errors of observation but was a genuine null result.

The special relativity interpretation of this conclusion idealized the situation to the extent that the effect of gravitation was omitted and the Earth was regarded as moving in a Euclidean straight line with constant speed during the very short time occupied by the experiment. It was then shown, firstly, that the hypothesis of the validity of Euclidean geometry could be retained but that the assumption of a single absolute time would have to be rejected. On the basis of these two postulates, a new theory of motion could be worked out from which the null result of the Michelson-Morley experiment could be predicted. More precisely, if there are two frames of reference for distance measurements, distances in each being established by identical procedures, and if the frames of reference are in constant relative motion as judged from either frame, then to each frame there must be associated a system of time-keeping of such a kind that the velocity of light has the same value relative to either frame.

The important points that are brought out by special relativity are, firstly, that there is no absolute theory of motion and of the associated dynamics and, secondly, that time and distance measurements can be much more closely interwoven than they are in classical physics. This interdependence results in the conclusion that two events* may be simultaneous in one frame of reference and not in another and also that the distance between two events is not an absolute but depends on the frame of reference relative to which it is measured. The device that is employed in relativity theory for interlocking closely time and distance measurements is to use what may be called a four-dimensional geometrical representation for all the events under contemplation. Each event is 'plotted', so to speak, as a 'point' having four, instead of three, co-ordinates; three of these fix the position in space of the event relative to some frame of reference, the fourth is a co-ordinate specifying the instant of occurrence of the event in the same frame of reference.

* In the language of relativity, an event is analogous to a point in space. As a point has no magnitude, so an event has neither magnitude in space nor duration in time.

The four-dimensional representation of events thus plotted is conveniently called *space-time* and it will be considered in more detail later in this chapter in connection with general relativity. Whether space-time has 'reality' or 'physical existence' is another question which could be answered only when these terms have been defined. The theoretical astronomer need not, however, await the production of an answer: space-time may be regarded as a mathematical device that is very valuable for purposes of calculation. It enables us to make predictions regarding the motions of astronomical bodies which can then be compared with observation. If agreement results, the concept of space-time is useful; if disagreement were ever to occur, then the notion would cease to have value.

In Chapter 2 we described the process by which local distance was measured, for example, the local distance of a planet. In this procedure it was taken for granted that the astronomers at the observatories A and B of fig. 1 made their observations simultaneously and that the local distance of P that resulted was absolute. But special relativity shows that simultaneity is dependent on the selection of some frame of reference; there is no absolute definition available. Nor is there any absolute definition of the distance between the two observatories. It might be thought that the frame of reference in which A and B were at rest, which may be called the zero frame, must be selected and that the time associated with this frame was the time kept by the observatory clocks. But one can imagine a second frame moving with uniform speed u with respect to the zero frame and then, in terms of the time appropriate to this new frame, the astronomers at A and B would not be carrying out their observations simultaneously and the distance from A to B would have a value that differed from that in the zero frame. This difference, special relativity predicts, would depend on the ratio of the square of u to the square of the velocity of light c.

Now it might be thought that these difficulties could be eliminated by simply asserting that the zero frame had priority over all others, but this cutting of the Gordian knot will not do, for there is another principle inherent in relativity to which reference has not yet been made. It is this: reference frames, even of the combined space and time variety used in relativity, are elements introduced into the description of the physical situation by the investigator and are therefore alterable by an act of his will. Nothing essential must therefore be made to depend on the choice of one reference frame rather than another; all reference frames must be on an equal footing; and we should fix attention on those conclusions that can be demonstrated to be equally valid in every reference frame. It happens that the distance between two events and the time interval between them are not characteristics possessing this invariant property. This is not to say that the practical steps by which the clocks in the observatories A and B are synchronized are meaningless. Nor does it mean that the sequence of observational steps by which the local distance of the planet P is determined make no sense. Rather is it true that the result is tied to the operational procedure and is relative to it; no guarantee is provided by the procedure that the resulting distance is an absolute quantity and that a different operating procedure would necessarily give the same result.

That the relativity of distance and time measurements of the kind contemplated by special relativity should not have been noticed in the solar system, the Galaxy and outwards to the nearby galaxies, is easily explained. The differences inherent in the use of one reference frame rather than another depend, as has been stated, on the ratio of the square of the relative velocity of the frames to the square of the velocity of light. In the solar system, where distances are most accurately determined, the relative velocities of objects rarely attain 70 miles per second, whereas the velocity of light is 186,000 miles per second. Thus the ratio of the squares of these velocities will be found to introduce changes in the distances that amount at most to one part in ten million. But the astronomical unit is determined to within the very much larger error of one part in five thousand. For objects in the Galaxy and for the nearer galaxies, even if relative velocities of up to 950 miles per second are allowed, the errors in the distances are so large that again no distinction need be made between one reference frame and another. Clearly, however, the large recessional velocities implied by the red-shift must give us pause: it is by no means self-evident that in the universe at large the differences between reference frames can be ignored.

General Relativity

From the physical point of view, general relativity differs from the special theory because it allows for the effects of gravitational fields in addition to those introduced by high velocities. The notion of space-time is still employed and it is now necessary to give more details about this mathematical device. Let us first consider a simple, two-dimensional Euclidean problem. If the co-ordinates of a point on a plane referred to a rectangular reference frame (x) are given by the numbers*x^1 and x^2, then a neighbouring point can be said to have the co-ordinates $(x^1 + dx^1)$ and $(x^2 + dx^2)$. The small differences dx^1 and dx^2 are called the differentials of the co-ordinates. Then, by Pythagoras' theorem, the distance between the two points (ds) is given by

$$ds^2 = (dx^1)^2 + (dx^2)^2.$$

* It is an unfortunate convention in relativity theory that the indices which distinguish one co-ordinate from another are written at the top of the main symbol. A power, say the square, of a co-ordinate has then to be written $(x^2)^2$.

Similarly, if we consider three dimensions, we give the point the co-ordinates (x^1, x^2, x^3) and the distance between two neighbouring points is given by

$$ds^2 = (dx^1)^2 + (dx^2)^2 + (dx^3)^2,$$

which we can write more briefly as

$$ds^2 = \sum_{\mu=1}^{3} (dx^\mu)^2.$$

Now, returning to the question of general relativity, the co-ordinates of an event in the reference frame (x) consist of the set of four numbers (x^4, x^1, x^2, x^3) of which the first specifies the time of occurrence of the event while the other three give its location in space. It is postulated in general, as in special, relativity that the same event could be described in a second reference frame (y) by the co-ordinates (y^4, y^1, y^2, y^3). But whereas the reference frames (x) and (y) are considered to be in uniform relative motion in special relativity, this restriction is removed in general relativity and the frames may move with respect to one another with a relative acceleration.

Every event is presumed to have at least one neighbouring event whose co-ordinates are $(x^4 + dx^4, x^1 + dx^1, x^2 + dx^2, x^3 + dx^3)$ in the reference frame (x). Again, the small differences dx^4, dx^1, dx^2, dx^3 are called the differentials of the co-ordinates. The absolute distance and absolute time of classical physics having been discarded in relativity, it is nevertheless necessary to postulate some quantity that is absolute in the sense that it has the same value in all reference frames. The quantity chosen to play this role denotes the absolute separation of an event from any one of its neighbours and it is called the *interval* between them. The interval is a compound of the time and space separations of the two events. But we must remember that in relativity we may have to make use of a geometry which is non-Euclidean. Hence the customary Euclidean formulae shown above cannot be used. Instead of simply summing the squares of the differentials we must also consider the various products of the differentials – that is, in addition to $(dx^1)^2$, $(dx^2)^2$, etc., we also consider $dx^1 dx^2$, $dx^1 dx^3$, etc. Further, in order to incorporate non-Euclidean geometry, we have to introduce in front of each such product a function of the co-ordinates, $g_{\mu\nu}$, where μ and ν each successively take the values 1 to 4. Thus the product $dx^1 dx^3$, for example, would be multiplied by $2g_{13}$, the factor 2 arising because it is also assumed that the functions $g_{\mu\nu}$ are symmetrical so that $g_{\mu\nu}=g_{\nu\mu}$. There is therefore a total of ten such functions. The equation we obtain for the interval ds is then

$$ds^2 = \sum_{\mu=1}^{4} \sum_{\nu=1}^{4} g_{\mu\nu}\, dx^\mu\, dx^\nu, \qquad (1)$$

and it is referred to as the *metric* of the space-time, the ten $g_{\mu\nu}$ being known as the *coefficients of the metric*. The specific mathematical forms of these coefficients depend partly on the reference frame employed and partly on the underlying geometry. If the reference frame is changed from (x) to (y) then for the same two events

$$ds^2 = \sum_{\mu=1}^{4} \sum_{\nu=1}^{4} \bar{g}_{\mu\nu}\, dy^\mu\, dy^\nu, \qquad (2)$$

where the $\bar{g}_{\mu\nu}$ are now functions of the new co-ordinates (y^4, y^1, y^2, y^3) but the numerical value of ds is unchanged. The coefficients of the metric play a fundamental role in the theory of space-time and are used to form a link with the properties of matter. Einstein does this in the following way, his argument consisting essentially of two parts, the first of which is a piece of pure mathematics in which the physical significance of the co-ordinates and of the coefficients of the metric is irrelevant, while the other brings in physical theory.

The general principle of relativity asserts that all sets of space-time co-ordinates are to be considered as equally valid. This means that one must find a means of re-expressing statements made in terms of one frame of reference in a form that will hold for any other specified frame. It would be agreeable if we could find enough mathematical entities which, like ds, remained invariant under the co-ordinate transformation. But this does not happen, and it would in any case be too restrictive. In addition to a certain number of invariants there do exist other mathematical entities which, while they do not remain unchanged under transformation, do at least change according to known rules. Such an entity has really already been encountered: it is the set of functions which form the coefficients of the metric ($g_{\mu\nu}$). This set constitutes what is known as a *tensor*, and the essential property of all tensors is that there are known rules for transforming them when passing from one co-ordinate system to another.

The tensor $g_{\mu\nu}$ is known as the *metrical tensor* and the next step is to form from it another tensor which involves not only the $g_{\mu\nu}$ but also their first and second derivatives with respect to the co-ordinates. This second tensor is known as the *Ricci tensor*; it is also constituted of ten symmetrical functions of the co-ordinates, $R_{\mu\nu}$. By combining the metrical and Ricci tensors in a certain fashion there is formed an invariant; it is called the *scalar curvature* and will be denoted by R^*.

Let us next consider, in any particular reference frame, the values of the metrical and Ricci tensors and of the scalar curvature at a point P and at any nearby point P'. The values at the two points will, in general, be different and, by a process familiar in the calculus of tensors, we can find the ratio of the differences of value to the interval separating P' from P. Then by allowing P' to approach P indefinitely closely it is possible to define the rates of change of the tensors and scalar curvature at P. Now the important fact is that a certain combination of these entities has a zero rate of change and this is a property that cannot be altered by changing the co-ordinate system. It is said to constitute a 'conservation law'. The combination is itself a tensor constituted of ten symmetrical functions of the co-ordinates, $E_{\mu\nu}$. It is known as the Einstein tensor and its mathematical expression is

$$E_{\mu\nu} = R_{\mu\nu} - \tfrac{1}{2}g_{\mu\nu}(R^* - 2\lambda). \tag{3}$$

The mathematical expression of the fact that this tensor obeys a conservation law is contained in the statement that the vectorial divergence of the Einstein tensor is zero. The proof that the tensor possesses this property involves, at one stage, a mathematical process equivalent to that of integration and this introduces into the expression for $E_{\mu\nu}$ the constant λ. Historically, Einstein first noticed that this constant of integration was present in the course of the solution of a cosmological problem. For this reason, the constant was given the name of the *cosmical constant* which has proved to be a most unfortunate name. It has led to the belief that the cosmical constant is produced in some way by the study of the universe. In fact the origin of the constant lies in a purely mathematical process and it would still be present in equation (3) even if no cosmological application of the Einstein tensor had ever been thought of. The value of the cosmical constant may be positive, zero or negative and the choice between these alternatives really belongs to the second, or physical, part of Einstein's argument. To this we now turn.

In classical mechanics, and particularly in the theories of hydrodynamics and of elasticity, it had been noticed that the physical properties of matter could be described by tensors constituted by ten symmetrical functions of the classical co-ordinates and the time. These tensors describe the amount of matter per unit volume (the density), the state of stress in the material, the velocity with which it moves, and so forth. A tensor of this kind is known as an *energy-tensor*. Moreover it was noticed that the fundamental equations governing the motion of the material could, in many cases, be stated in the succinct form that the vectorial divergence of the energy-tensor was zero. Thus for a perfect fluid moving under the action of its own pressure-gradient only, the flow is governed by equations stating that the vectorial divergence of the energy-tensor of the perfect fluid vanishes. Einstein then made the following physical hypothesis: suppose that a distribution of matter is described by an energy-tensor $T\mu\nu$ which possesses the property of having a vanishing vectorial divergence. Suppose also that a certain space-time is to describe this distribution of matter. Then let it be assumed that the Einstein tensor for this space-time is proportional to the energy-tensor *precisely because* both tensors have vanishing vectorial divergences. The constant of proportionality was taken to involve the universal constant of gravitation G and the result of Einstein's assumption was his ten field equations

$$R_{\mu\nu} - \tfrac{1}{2}g_{\mu\nu}\,(R^* - 2\lambda) = -8\pi\,G\,T_{\mu\nu}. \tag{4}$$

They imply that there is a connection between the nature and motion of the material under contemplation and the coefficients of the metric of that particular space-time which corresponds to the distribution of matter. Einstein quickly showed that gravitational effects were in this way intrinsically incorporated into the description of the behaviour of the material and, indeed, that the classical theory of Newtonian gravitation could be obtained as a first approximation from his field equations. Furthermore a detailed examination of the field equations shows that the cosmical constant represents a general force acting on all matter in the universe. If λ is a positive number, the force is one of repulsion driving all particles of matter away from one another. If λ is negative, the force is attractive and, like gravitation, tends to bring all particles of matter closer together. This λ-force, as it will be called, must be so small that it exerts no significant effect in situations where gravitation is the dominant factor. Thus it must be small enough to produce no observable effects in the motion of the planets of the solar system or in those of double stars. Indeed it will be shown in a later chapter that the cosmical constant has a role to play only when the universe as a whole is considered.

The distinction between special and general relativity is also conveniently explained here. The space-time of special relativity has a metric of the form

$$ds^2 = (dx^4)^2 - \left\{(dx^1)^2 + (dx^2)^2 + (dx^3)^2\right\}/c^2, \qquad (5)$$

when a co-ordinate system of the kind called inertial* is used. A transformation to another inertial system – that must be in uniform motion with respect to the first – preserves the form of the metric, which becomes

$$ds^2 = (dy^4)^2 - \left\{(dy^1)^2 + (dy^2)^2 + (dy^3)^2\right\}/c^2. \qquad (6)$$

In these formulae c is the (constant) velocity of light and therefore the coefficients of the metric are also all constants. It can then be proved that the Ricci tensor and the scalar curvature are identically zero for the space-time of special relativity. Thus in Einstein's equations (4) it is necessary to assume that the terms in λ and in G are also negligibly small. This leads to the conclusion that special relativity will be useful in physical situations where the λ-force and gravitational forces are both negligibly small. In practice, such is found to be the case, the theory having its most important applications in atomic physics where electromagnetic effects are dominant.

---

* Suppose that one or more particles of matter are in motion because of their interaction with a given system of physical bodies. An inertial system of co-ordinates is then one relative to which the motions of the particles are unaccelerated. Such systems can occur even in cases in which an observer, contemplating the whole situation from outside it, would say that the particles were subjected to non-zero forces due to the presence of the other bodies.

In the technical language of mathematics, the vanishing of the Ricci tensor and the scalar curvature in the space-time of special relativity are consequences of a property that it possesses called 'flatness'. The space-times of general relativity are, in contrast, 'curved', which means that at one event in space-time at least the Ricci tensor and the scalar curvature do not vanish. It is the possession of this property that makes curved space-times suitable for the description of gravitational effects and for those of the λ-force. An easy non-mathematical explanation of the technical terms 'flat' and 'curved' is hard to find. The words themselves have so many connotations that their use in this highly technical sense is itself misleading. One can but try to use an analogy drawn from geometrical manifolds of two, instead of four, dimensions. The Euclidean plane is one such two-dimensional manifold, the surface of a sphere is another; the former possesses the geometrical attribute of flatness, the latter, that of curvature. This difference manifests itself in the geometries appropriate to the two surfaces. Thus in the Euclidean plane, straight lines are of infinite length, the three angles of a triangle have a sum equal to π, the sum of the squares on the two sides of a right-angled triangle is equal to the square on the hypotenuse, and so on. On the surface of a sphere, great circles are the analogues of straight lines and they are of finite length equal to the circumference of the sphere, the angles of a spherical triangle do not have a sum equal to π, and Pythagoras' theorem in the form stated above is no longer true. The four-dimensional space-times of general relativity differ from one another and from that employed in special relativity in analogous but far more complicated ways. This is not only because four, as against two, dimensions give rise to greater intricacy but also because one of the dimensions is interpreted physically as referring to the time-relations between events. Whether the resulting 'curvature' of space-time is the 'cause' of gravitation, as is often stated, is a question on which judgement can be reserved until the matter of the 'physical reality' of space-time has been satisfactorily resolved. Meanwhile there is nothing to prevent the use of general relativity as a technique in mathematical astronomy.

The last of the properties of the curved space-times of general relativity that must be noticed is a very important one. In any small region of space and for a short interval of time, the space-time is locally identifiable with the flat space-time of special relativity. Though this is true in any local region, the tying together of the special relativity space-times appropriate to two regions widely separated in space, or in time, or in both ways at once, has to be done through the underlying curved space-time, if it can be done at all. But the existence of this local property is sufficient to guarantee that the advantages gained in the treatment of high velocities by the use of special relativity will also be taken over into general relativity.

World-lines

A given distribution of matter will have an associated space-time the coefficients of whose metric will have been found by the mathematical operation known as solving Einstein's equations (4) above. This purely mathematical process gives each coefficient as a specific function of the co-ordinates of some reference frame. Usually the material contemplated will be in motion and, speaking classically, this motion will be due to the action of gravitational forces, forces due to internal stresses, the λ-force, etc., which are implicit in the Einstein equations. It is possible to fix attention on one particle of the material and to note down, relative to some reference frame (x), its spatial position at successive instants of the time appropriate to the reference frame. Each one of these space and time readings can be plotted as a 'point' in the four-dimensional geometrical manifold that is the space-time.

Though the human imagination is incapable of picturing such a sequence of four-dimensional points, they can be described mathematically by equations and can be regarded as lying on a curve in four dimensions. This is called the *world-line* of the particle. When, however, a new reference frame (*y*) is employed in the same way to trace out the history of the motion of the same particle in the same space-time, the equations specifying its world-line usually have quite a different appearance from what they had when the frame (*x*) was used. This is familiar in classical mechanics also. For example, consider a particle moving at a constant speed along a straight line relative to a fixed rectangular co-ordinate system. Another system may be selected which rotates at a constant angular rate about the origin of the original one. Then, in the rotating frame, the path of the particle will be a complicated spiral. The question then arises: are there any world-lines which are in some way intrinsically connected with the metric of the space-time and therefore with the forces acting on the particle? This intrinsic connection is to mean that the world-line is defined in the same basic way in all reference frames. The only quantity which is independent of reference frames is the interval *ds* and so it is used in the definition of world-lines of this kind. They are called *geodesics* and they exist in all space-times. The characteristic property of geodesics can be described as follows. If we measure the interval between two points *P* and *Q* along a certain path joining them and again along another, nearby path, the two measurements will, of course, differ. If we consider a series of nearby paths the interval from *P* to *Q* will change continuously from path to path. However it can be proved that there exists a certain path joining *P* and *Q* such that the interval is either a maximum or a minimum as compared with nearby paths. It is then said that the interval has a stationary value along this particular path. We now define a geodesic as a curve, the interval between any two points of which has a stationary value as compared with the interval measured along any nearby curve passing through the same two points. This is one of the properties of the straight line in a Euclidean space and therefore the geodesic is the analogue of the straight line of elementary geometry. It is absolute in the sense that it is intrinsically unaffected by the particular reference frame in terms of which its equations may be written down. An additional step taken in general relativity is to assert that the geodesics of space-time are the world-lines of those particles which are moving freely under the action of the forces implicit in the coefficients of the metric. If a particle has a world-line which is not a geodesic, it must be influenced by some constraint which is not recorded in the coefficients. The notion may seem to be very far fetched but the geodesic principle has been verified for the particular space-time which describes the gravitational field of the sun. If Mercury and the other planets are regarded as having geodesic world-lines in this space-time, it can be predicted that the perihelia of their orbits will move in space in a certain way and this motion is confirmed by observation. The effect had been noticed before the advent of general relativity though Newtonian gravitational theory had failed to interpret it.

The motion of light in general relativity follows from the local validity of special relativity. In that theory a photon which moves through a distance

$$dl = \left\{ (dx^1)^2 + (dx^2)^2 + (dx^3)^2 \right\}^{1/2}$$

in time dx^4 does so with speed c. Hence $c\,dx^4 = dl$ and reference to equation (5) then shows that the corresponding value of ds is zero. The vanishing of the interval is again an invariant property. Moreover, a space-time of general relativity can be regarded in principle as the result of stringing together a sequence of local special relativity space-times. In each of these the interval along the path of a photon will be zero and therefore it will still be zero in the underlying general relativity space-time, because, whatever else may be modified, the interval is unchanging and absolute. It is therefore said in general relativity that the world-line of a photon is a *null-geodesic*, which simply means a certain curve in four dimensions along which the measure of the interval is zero. This conclusion is as true for a wave theory of light as for a corpuscular; in the former case the null-geodesic can be proved to be the analogue of the normal to the wave-front of classical theory.

The equations of the null-geodesics involve the coefficients of the metric and these, in general relativity, depend on the gravitational and other forces implicit in Einstein's equations. Hence it is predicted that the motion of light will, in particular, be affected by the gravitational fields through which the light passes, a radically new conclusion as compared with classical physics. That this is so has again been verified for the gravitational field of the Sun in the phenomenon known as the bending of light-rays. This phenomenon also shows that the paths of light-rays in empty space can be different from Euclidean straight lines.

Links between Theory and Observation

The first step in finding the space-time appropriate to a given distribution of matter consists in solving Einstein's equations. This is usually a very difficult mathematical operation and only one method has so far yielded results. It is a procedure often used in classical mechanics and it may be illustrated by means of an example. Suppose that we find a piece of iron of quite arbitrary and jagged shape, with internal cavities and with lumps of lead embedded in it. Suppose also that the piece of iron has one sharp point on its surface. This object is presented to an applied mathematician and he is told that it is to be spun like a top about the sharp point. Would he be good enough to calculate beforehand what the motion of the object will be like? The mathematician will undoubtedly say that the problem presented to him is too complicated for analysis. But he will equally certainly offer to substitute for it another problem with which he can deal. In this one, the top will have an axis through the sharp point and it will be symmetrical, both as to shape and as to internal constitution, with respect to this axis. The concealed cavities and lumps of lead hidden within the top will be imagined as being symmetrically arranged about the axis. The high degree of physical symmetry thus postulated will be reflected in the mathematical equations that govern the motion. A simplification of the equations will result which makes them amenable to analysis and will thus yield a solution. From his past experience, the mathematician will assert that most of the essentials of the motion of the actual piece of iron will be predictable by considering the idealized symmetrical top.

A similar process of idealization is employed in general relativity. Highly symmetrical distributions of matter are imagined, such as a perfectly spherical star in otherwise empty space, or a universe filled with a continuous uniform material. The coefficients of the metric describe the physical properties of the imagined distribution of matter and the forces controlling its motion. The coefficients will therefore possess mathematical properties of symmetry corresponding to the physical ones. These symmetry conditions are in turn often sufficient to identify the possible frames of reference and the co-ordinates appropriate to each. The energy-tensor of very symmetrical distributions of matter will also be assignable from past experience with classical mechanics. Taking all these considerations together, it has been found in practice possible to solve Einstein's equations and thus to obtain the space-time appropriate to the imagined distribution of matter.

It also sometimes happens that the symmetry properties alone are sufficient to determine the coefficients of the metric almost completely. In such a case, the left-hand sides of Einstein's equations (4) can be evaluated and used to find the energy-tensor of the corresponding material. An illustration of this type of procedure is provided by the cosmology of general relativity, as will become clear in the sequel.

If, in general relativity, this idealizing and symmetrizing device is employed, it is still necessary to point out that the application of the theory is not restricted to physical situations of this kind. This is particularly true in the cosmological applications where extremely symmetrized distributions of matter have hitherto been considered because of their mathematical tractability. It is indeed only in recent years that the first attempts to escape from these extreme simplifications have begun and investigators have searched for idealizations lying a little closer to the tremendous complexity presented by the universe which is observed.

There is another aspect of the problem of linking theory and observation to which we must refer. When a space-time has once been worked out, it is usually the case that the co-ordinate system in which the results are expressed has no immediate physical significance. By this is meant that the spatial co-ordinates do not correspond directly with distances measured by astronomers. As an illustration, suppose that it is required to find out in what way the theoretical co-ordinates assigned to a light source are to be related to its apparent magnitude, which, for a galaxy, is normally the only indication of distance. The absolute local distance l of equation (7), Chapter 2, no longer exists in the space-time; but a little reflection shows that the connection between l and apparent magnitude is made in classical physics through the property that the intensity of a light source falls off as the inverse square of l. Therefore, by an analysis of the null-geodesic world-lines of light-rays, a quantity called 'luminosity-distance' is found which also has the property that the intensity of a light source diminishes according to the inverse square of this luminosity-distance. It can then be safely assumed that it is luminosity-distance which is given by measurements of apparent magnitude combined with estimates of absolute magnitude. It turns out that this method not only can allow for the relative motion of source and observer, but also for the effects of gravitational fields. In addition the definition of distance is clearly tied to a specific observational procedure for measuring it.

Another consequence of the notion that distance should be tied to the operation by which it is to be measured is that a particular observer may assign more than one 'distance' to a given object. This differs from the special relativity conclusion that two *different* observers in uniform relative motion may assign different values to the distance between two given objects, even if the same operational method of measurement is employed. In general relativity, an observer may, for example, determine the luminosity-distances between himself and a number of light sources. He would do this by measuring apparent magnitudes. The light sources may, however, all have one and the same small linear size. The same observer could then also measure the apparent angular diameters of the light sources and use this new measurement to compute 'distance'. It can be proved that the 'distance by apparent size' found in this way is different from luminosity-distance, in certain circumstances at least. The theoretical co-ordinates of a source in the space-time are, of course, the same in both cases: it is the different measuring operations which give rise to the different distances. Since one kind of measurement cannot be regarded as 'better' or 'truer' than another, there is no way of preferring one kind of distance to another. Moreover relativity theory is so constructed that all these different types of distance are equal to one another provided that the object is close to the observer and moving with respect to him with a velocity which is small compared with that of light. From the relativity point of view, it is this property of distance that permitted classical astronomers to use, without running into contradictions, the concept of local distance in the solar system, the Galaxy and even for galaxies neighbouring our own.

The question of the physical identification of time-co-ordinates in a space-time of general relativity is usually carried out in a much more naive fashion. A reference frame and its associated time can as a rule be found in terms of which the development of the physical situation under contemplation takes on its simplest mathematical expression. This particular time is then, by definition, equated with the ephemeris time described in Chapter 2. That this is in fact the actual procedure is evidenced by the custom of expressing all time-intervals in years or in seconds. These units would be meaningless unless the theoretical time-co-ordinate had, at some stage in the argument, been identified with ephemeris time. There is, of course, nothing objectionable in this procedure; if some entirely inappropriate time-co-ordinate had been selected it would be expected that contradictions with observation would, sooner or later, reveal themselves.

Kinematical Relativity and the Steady-State Theory

The application of general relativity to cosmology has involved the assumption of a far greater degree of symmetry in the idealization studied than is found in the observed universe. But this is not a consequence of the theory itself; it is merely a device for reducing the number of mathematical difficulties. A different situation is encountered in two alternative theories which have been developed during the last thirty years. The first of these was the kinematical relativity [30] of

E. A. Milne, originally proposed in 1933. In this theory a high degree of uniformity and of symmetry was postulated as a fundamental property of the observed universe. It was taken to be self-evidently true that astronomers, wherever they might be located in the universe, would see the same general sequence of events as we do from the earth. This idea was named the cosmological principle. By its very nature it is unverifiable – because no astronomer has ever viewed the universe except from the earth – yet it has been regarded as a principle to which the universe must conform. A second feature of kinematical relativity which was found very attractive was its use of the space-time and mathematical framework of special relativity. Thus the curved space-times of general relativity and the struggles involved in dealing with Einstein's equations appeared to be happily avoided. A third, and possibly the most valuable and attractive feature of this theory, was the emphasis placed on a clear definition of the term distance. Milne contended that a precise operational definition was required and the one he chose was essentially radar distance. An observer sends a burst of radiation towards the astronomical object whose distance he wants to determine, and notes the time on his clock at which the signal starts. He also notes the instant of the return of the reflected signal. Then by definition the distance of the object is half the difference between the readings on the clock multiplied by the (constant) velocity of light. However, there was a difficulty here because there should be no absolute way of regulating the rate at which the observer's clock is working. Any clock therefore, working at any arbitrary rate, should be equally suitable for the purpose of determining radar distance, and this feature Milne also incorporated into his theory.

Kinematical relativity sought to describe the universe as a whole first of all and then come down to the problem of gravitation. It was here that it ran into difficulties. Something like Newton's theory of gravitation was eventually produced, but at the price of having to suppose that the universal constant of gravitation, G, was in fact variable with time. For this conclusion, no observational evidence could be adduced. Furthermore, the equivalence of times proceeding at different rates and all as good as one another had a curious consequence. It was possible to prove that the radar distance from the observer to a particular object either varied with time or remained constant according to the rate at which the observer chose to make his clock go. Thus the red-shift could not be unambiguously interpreted as an effect of relative velocity. Apart from this theory of time, kinematical relativity was presently shown to be a special case of the cosmology of general relativity. In this special case, gravitational effects and those of the λ-force are regarded as negligibly small, the motion of expansion proceeding unimpeded by the action of any forces. Though Milne's theory has as a whole been abandoned during the past ten years, the emphasis he laid on the necessity for clear operational definitions for such notions as distance and time must be regarded as a valuable contribution to cosmology.

The steady-state [31], or creation of matter, theory of cosmology was first proposed by Bondi and Gold in 1948 and was further developed by Hoyle. As in kinematical relativity, uniformity and symmetry are again taken as fundamental properties of the observed universe. But these notions are pushed to their ultimate extremes. It is now asserted that astronomers, wherever they may be located in the universe and at whatever time they may make their observations, necessarily obtain identical pictures of the universe. If this is to be so, then an immediate difficulty is encountered: in an expanding universe, the number-density of galaxies necessarily falls as the time goes on. Therefore a given observer could locate himself in time by noting how the number-density changed. To prevent this, a supply of new galaxies in every unit volume must be imagined. This is done by assuming that hydrogen atoms are created out of nothing, that these atoms collect themselves into galaxies and that all this happens at just the requisite rate to keep the number-density of galaxies constant. Another consequence of the high degree of uniformity and symmetry is that the rate of expansion must be an absolute constant of nature. For, if the rate varied with time, its variation would presumably be detectable and would again provide a means for locating oneself in time.

The space-time employed by Bondi and Gold closely resembles that of a special case of the cosmology of general relativity, the so-called de Sitter universe. The laws of the propagation of light and the theory of world-lines are the same as in general relativity. But because of the creation of matter hypothesis the general relativity laws of the conservation of mass and momentum are discarded. It is argued that these laws have been established through the study of small-scale systems such as are found in the laboratory, the solar system or our own Galaxy. In the universe at large they need not hold; moreover it is shown that the required rate of creation of hydrogen atoms is so small that it could not be detected locally.

As originally formulated by Bondi and Gold, the steady-state theory contained no theory of gravitation. Hoyle [32] has made two attempts, in 1948 and again in 1960, to remedy this defect by modifying Einstein's field equations (equations (4) above) which incorporate the general relativity theory of gravitation. In the new field equations the cosmical constant is assumed to be zero and a new tensor, $C_{\mu\nu}$, is introduced, which depends on the rate of creation of matter. The Einstein tensor without the cosmical constant is $E_{\mu\nu} = R_{\mu\nu} - \frac{1}{2}R^* g_{\mu\nu}$ and Hoyle's field equations are then

$$E_{\mu\nu} + C_{\mu\nu} = -8\pi G T_{\mu\nu}. \tag{7}$$

In these field equations the energy-tensor no longer satisfies a conservation law, though the Einstein tensor necessarily continues to do so.

When, in the next chapter, we come to discuss the notion of uniformity as it is used in cosmology, an idea will be employed that is suggested by the steady-state theory. It is that the properties of sources of radiation, including their number-density, may vary intrinsically with the time, quite apart from any changes that may be due to the general motion of expansion. Apart from this point, further discussion of the steady-state theory must be delayed until the fusion of the observational data with general relativity and the alternative theories of cosmology has been considered.

Chapter 5

Model Universes and the Red-shift

The discussion of the observational data on the distribution in space of the galaxies, which was given in Chapter 3, led to the conclusion that there was roughly the same amount of matter in each unit volume of space provided that this volume was sufficiently large. This followed from the assumption that the galaxies were spread out in the Euclidean space of classical physics and were not moving with respect to one another. But the red-shift phenomenon also led to the contradictory conclusion that the galaxies were moving with high velocities with respect to our own. It is now necessary to clear up this difficulty and this will be done, in the first instance, through the medium of the theory of general relativity [33]. The first problem to be settled is the following: if the galaxies are in relative motion, what meaning can be attached to the statement that they are uniformly distributed in space, when account is taken of the possibility that space itself may not be Euclidean? To answer this question it is necessary to define carefully what is meant by the notion of uniformity.

Uniformity

The first step which the reader must take is to disabuse his mind of the widely held idea that uniformity necessarily implies the existence of Euclidean space and of objects evenly spread out in it and at mutual rest. This is indeed a possible definition but it is only one among many; it is certainly not the one employed in cosmology. Whether cosmology is based on general relativity, kinematical relativity or the steady-state theory, the procedure adopted is the following: suppose that a description of a moving system of objects can be constructed mathematically in such a way that an over-all time, applicable to all parts of the system, is an essential element of the description. Then consider, for example, the number-density of the bodies of the system – the galaxies for instance. If this number-density *varies with the time alone* then it must follow, firstly, that at a given instant the number-density is the same at all points of space, because, by hypothesis, the number-density is independent of position. Thus the number-density is instantaneously constant throughout space, and this is true whatever the geometrical character of space may be. But, secondly, the number-densities at two *different* instants of time will, in general, be unequal. The number-density of galaxies, if they are flying apart, will decrease as time proceeds from this cause alone. But it is possible to imagine that galaxies are forming and dissolving again; in this case the number-density will vary intrinsically with time, apart from the expansion effect. In the sense in which the term is employed in cosmology, a *uniform* number-density will be one which changes with the time alone, whether this change is due solely to the relative motions of the constituent bodies of the system or to intrinsic variations as well. The history of a distribution of objects of uniform number-density will therefore consist of a continuous passage from one instantaneous state of constant number-density to another whose (constant) number-density may have a different value. By the term 'constant' is here meant 'having the same value at all points of space', whether space is Euclidean or not.

This concept of uniformity can be applied to other properties of the constituent objects of the system. Consider one of their physical characteristics such as temperature, or intrinsic output of light, or absolute power-output of radio waves. The collection of objects will be said to be uniform with respect to this characteristic if it varies only with the time – or of course simply remains constant – and also if it varies in the same way for all the objects. For example, if the temperature of each of the objects is T_1 at time t_1 then at time t_2 the temperature has the same value T_2 for each object though it may be that T_1 is not equal to T_2. The mathematical expression of this state of affairs is to say that the temperature is the same function of the time for every object. A physical characteristic behaving in this way will be said to possess the U-property.

It must be confessed that a system of uniform objects uniformly distributed in space in the foregoing sense seems to be taking us very far from the universe of galaxies which astronomical observation reveals. Far more regularity is being assumed than appears to exist in nature. It is therefore useful to distinguish between the observed universe with its galaxies differing intrinsically from one another, with inhomogeneities of distribution in space and all the other observed irregularities, and a model universe whose contents have all the uniformity that can be desired. Whether or not such model universes can, in fact, play a useful part in the understanding of the observed universe is a question that can only be answered at the end of our inquiry. In this respect the crucial criterion for accepting or rejecting a model universe will be agreement or disagreement with observation.

Model Universes

The feature of the observed universe which perhaps presents the most formidable obstacle to the mathematical astronomer is the discreteness in the distribution of matter. Galaxies are separated from one another by regions which, if not entirely vacuous, contain far less matter per unit volume than occurs within galaxies. And on a larger scale clusters of galaxies occupy regions where the average density of matter must be higher than elsewhere. In a model universe therefore the simplification adopted is to replace the discrete galaxies by a continuous material which may be called the representative gas. This gas is uniform however small the unit of volume may be; there is no lower limit to such a volume below which inhomogeneity sets in. The representative gas has the advantage over the distribution of matter in the observed universe in that its properties are simple to describe. The essential ones are two in number and both are regarded as possessing the U-property. They are the density of the gas, which is the mass per unit volume, and the internal stress or pressure. These characteristics will be discussed in detail later. It is first necessary to deal with the general theory of such a gas when it is assumed to be in motion.

Since a model universe is regarded as filled with representative gas whose density and pressure are to possess the U-property, there must be an over-all time with respect to which these properties are to vary. Now it is a basic postulate of general relativity that the space-time for the model universe must reflect the properties of its material content. In order to see where this notion leads us, we may subdivide the question and consider, firstly, the state of affairs at a particular instant and, secondly, the way in which the properties of space-time are to vary from moment to moment. At a particular instant the portions of representative gas contained in two equal volumes of space are alike in the sense that, if these portions are interchanged, no alteration in the over-all situation occurs. From the space-time point of view this is translated into the statement that the geometry of space must be such that equal volumes must be interchangeable. Spaces possessing this property are known from geometrical theory where they are called spaces of constant curvature. One of these is the familiar Euclidean space whose geometry we study at school; its curvature is zero and it is therefore a flat space. But there are two other kinds as well, of a less familiar sort. The space of positive curvature, or spherical space, is the analogue in three dimensions of the two-dimensional surface of a sphere. The latter has no edge or boundary and yet it has a finite surface area. So in a spherical space, there is no boundary but nevertheless the total volume of space is finite. There are for example only a finite number of cubic miles which the objects in such a space could occupy. The third type of space is the hyperbolic, or space of negative curvature. Like the other two it also has no boundary but it shares with Euclidean space the property of having an infinite volume. Very crudely, indeed, the three kinds of space can be distinguished from each other in the following way with reference to volume. Within a large sphere of given radius, the volume is least if space is spherical, intermediate in amount if it is Euclidean and greatest of all when it is hyperbolic.

At each instant, space in our model universe must be of constant curvature. Now the properties of the representative gas change with time alone, the gas as a whole remaining similar to itself but on a different scale from moment to moment. This must also be reflected in the geometrical characteristics of space-time. Imagine eight marked particles of the gas which, at some instant, are located at the four corners of a cube. If the gas is moving in such a way that these particles are receding from one another, then the cube they mark out at some later instant will be larger than the initial cube. The postulate of uniformity implies that all volumes defined in this way – by the particles of the gas itself – will change by the same factor from one instant of time to the next. In other words, there will be a unique time-varying scale-factor R, applicable to all volumes. If indeed a volume is of magnitude dv at the instant when R is equal to unity, it will be of amount R^3dv at some other instant. Naturally it is in practice impossible to 'mark' the particles of the gas, but it is mathematically possible to define co-ordinate systems which describe the location of elements of the gas and which have the property of being co-moving, i.e. of following, so to speak, each gas-element as it moves.

This qualitative description of the way in which the space-time of a model universe is built up can be made mathematically precise by methods which are beyond the scope of this book. Suffice it to say that the final result is a formula for the metric, viz:

$$ds^2 = dt^2 - \frac{R^2(t)}{c^2} \left\{ \frac{dr^2 + r^2d\theta^2 + r^2\sin^2\theta\ d\phi^2}{(1 + kr^2/4)^2} \right\} \tag{1}$$

which is, of course, a particular case of (1), Chapter 4. The co-ordinates which were there called (x^4, x^1, x^2, x^3) are now written respectively (t, r, θ, ϕ) and t is the time with respect to which uniformity is defined. They are a co-moving system and since they thus follow the motion of the gas, the latter has zero velocity relative to the reference frame. In all equations that relate physically measurable quantities it is necessary that every term shall be expressed in the same units of length, time and mass. Hence, in equation (1), we suppose that s and t are measured in units of time and that some unit of length is also selected. Then the velocity of light, c, is expressed as a multiple of the unit of length divided by the same unit of time that was employed for s and t. If now R is expressed in multiplies of the unit of length, the ratio R/c will involve a multiple of the time unit alone. Thus the radial co-ordinate r can be regarded as a numerical multiplier (pure number) so that it is rR which represents a length. The angles θ and ϕ are, of course, also pure numbers because of the definition of circular measure. The formula (1) also contains the pure number k, known as the space-curvature constant, because its value characterizes the nature of the curvature of space. At this point it is necessary to distinguish between the curvature of space-time, which is a four-dimensional geometrical manifold, and the curvature of space, which is three-dimensional. The former depends on both R and the constant k, the latter is essentially given by k alone. It is important to remember that the curvature of space-time and the curvature of space are not identical; space may, for example, be flat and Euclidean but this is compatible with a space-time curvature. It is difficult to envisage such a situation in terms of four and three dimensions; therefore an analogy from geometrical manifolds of two and one dimensions may be useful. The surface of a cylinder is a curved two-dimensional geometrical manifold. Yet on its surface may be drawn straight lines parallel to the axis of the cylinder. These are geometrical manifolds of one dimension, i.e. of dimensions one lower than that of the surface, and they are uncurved. In a similar, but much more elaborate, fashion there can be spaces (three-dimensional) with one kind of curvature 'drawn in' or 'cut out from' space-time (four-dimensional) of a different curvature.

The space-curvature constant k in equation (1) has the values $+1, 0$ or -1 according as space is spherical, Euclidean or hyperbolic. Since these three values of k appear to be entirely capricious, it is worth looking at the matter in more detail. Consider the points in space for which $r = 1, 2, 3, 4, \ldots$ and suppose that the unit of length chosen for R is the yard. If it is decided to re-label these same points with the numbers $1/3, 2/3, 1, 4/3, \ldots$ respectively, then it is said that the co-ordinate-transformation $\bar{r} = r/3$ has been performed. The equation (1) becomes, as a result of the co-ordinate-transformation,

$$ds^2 = dt^2 - \frac{(3R)^2}{c^2} \left\{ \frac{d\bar{r}^2 + \bar{r}^2 d\theta^2 + \bar{r}^2 \sin^2\theta d\phi^2}{(1 + (9k)\bar{r}^2/4)^2} \right\} . \tag{2}$$

Thus the equations (1) and (2) would have the same mathematical form if a new space-curvature constant, $\bar{k}$, and a new scale-factor $\bar{R}$ were introduced, where

$$\bar{k}=9k, \quad \bar{R}=3R.$$

Hence if k is $+1$, 0 or -1, then $\bar{k}$ is 9, 0 or -9 and concomitantly the unit of length for $\bar{R}$ would be one-third of a yard, or one foot. In other words, the unit of length for R and the unit of numbering for r can always be chosen so that k can take on the values $+n$, 0 or $-n$, where n is an arbitrary positive number. Conversely, matters can always be arranged in such a fashion that n shall be unity, and as mentioned above this is the arrangement adopted.

The general assumption of uniformity therefore leads to a metric which contains one undetermined constant, namely, k. In general relativity, at least, it is not regarded as possible to pick out one of the three values of k in preference to the other two without more information than uniformity provides. But the theory also leads to another indeterminacy: the scale-factor R is *some* function of the time t and what specific function it may be is left open. The physical meaning of this imprecision in R is the following: suppose that of two particles of the gas, one is always at $r=0$, the other always at $r=\epsilon$, where ϵ is so small that its square and higher powers can be neglected. Then it can be proved from (1) that the distance apart of these two particles is $R\epsilon$ and that their relative velocity and acceleration are respectively, $R'\epsilon$ and $R''\epsilon$, where a prime (′) denotes a derivative with respect to t. Thus, in spite of the fixity of ϵ, the two particles can be in relatively accelerated motion. The fact that the theory does not give R as a specific function of t simply means that there are many different ways in which the representative gas could move without violating the fundamental property of uniformity. Limiting R to some particular function of t and choosing one of the three values for k require additional information either from observational sources or from preconceived ideas about what the universe 'ought' to be like. When this information is available a 'particular model universe' becomes available which means one wherein R is a specific function of t and one of the three possible values of k has been chosen. Among the threefold infinity of particular model universes there are some that are mathematically far more simple than the rest, though mathematical simplicity is unfortunately no guarantee of adequacy from the astronomical point of view. The simplest of all the particular models is probably the one originally brought into prominence by Milne in his kinematic relativity. It is defined by the equations

$$R=ct, \ k=-1, \tag{3}$$

which mean that the scale-factor increases proportionately to the time and that space is hyperbolic and therefore of infinite extent. This is a useful particular model for illustrative purposes.

Special World-Lines

In replacing the discrete galaxies of the observed universe by the representative gas, one of the features that is lost is a galaxy's individuality as a source of light or of radio waves. To recover this feature it is necessary to define what is to be meant by a source of radiation in a model universe. This is done by asserting that sources of radiation are those particles of the representative gas which have world-lines of a certain specially simple kind. Along any one of these special world-lines the co-ordinates r, θ and ϕ are constants and the time t is equal to the interval s (not distance) measured along the world-line. Much of the subsequent argument will turn on this identification because it is as sources of radiation that astronomical objects are studied in the first instance. Now every particle of the representative gas does not have a special world-line; hence whatever the particles of the representative gas may be, they cannot be the galaxies themselves. For if they were, then any world-line would be a possible one for a source of radiation in the model universe and this would contradict the identification that has been made. How then is the representative gas to be regarded from the physical point of view? The answer to this question which is suggested here is the following: the representative gas is the product of an imagined instantaneous disintegration of all the observed galaxies into their constituent atoms, the resulting material being imagined as spread out evenly in space. Thus the density of the gas at the present moment can be plausibly identified with the average density of matter in our, cosmically speaking, neighbourhood. It is to be hoped that this replacement of a continuous fluid having the same average density as that obtained from the masses of the galaxies and their estimated distances apart will reproduce the effects of gravitation in the universe. As to the pressure in the model universe, we may regard it as the counterpart of all those forms of energy in the observed universe that are not described as mass. The internal energies of stars and interstellar gas clouds, their kinetic and gravitational potential energies, the kinetic energies of galaxies due to their random motions over and above the general motion of expansion, are examples of these forms of non-material energy. All this energetic content of the observed universe is to be conceived of as distributed evenly among the products of the imagined disintegration. This energy will give rise to a motion of agitation of the individual particles of the gas and the result will be a gas pressure analogous to the pressure of a quantity of gas in a container in the laboratory. In addition the pressure in the model universe can, if desired, include the average pressure of radiation* in the observed universe.

* Electromagnetic waves carry momentum with them in the sense

It is also convenient at this point to identify the physical nature of the time t that occurs in the expression for the metric (1). In accordance with the procedure described in Chapter 4 this time is defined to be identical with, i.e. to proceed at the same rate as, the ephemeris time of Chapter 2. This definition may seem to be arbitrary and over-simplified but it is the one in fact used by cosmologists who always express time-intervals in years. It has been argued by some cosmologists that the time t should be defined by means of observations of the motions of nearby galaxies. Unfortunately this attractive notion has no operational content for a human astronomer for the very good reason that observation has not revealed any 'motion' of a galaxy. As has already been pointed out, the galaxies show no relative changes of position, no changes in apparent size nor do they reveal any phenomenon, save one, which would make us suspect that they were in motion at all. The exception is the red-shift; but the displacement of a spectral line furnishes by itself no method of time-keeping; no clock can be set to run at a certain rate simply by measuring the displacements found in spectral lines. It is for this reason that cosmologists, whatever they may say in purely theoretical terms, always express time-intervals in terms of ephemeris time.

Model Universes and the Red-shift

The picture which we, as human astronomers, have of the universe of galaxies is obtained from one location only, namely the earth. In addition it can be regarded as a picture obtained at a single instant of time, paradoxical as this may

that when they impinge on a material object, they produce an effect analogous to the impact of a bullet or other projectile. A region of space filled with electromagnetic waves travelling in all directions would thus exert a pressure roughly analogous to the pressure that would be exerted had the region been occupied by randomly moving particles of a gas.

seem to be. It is true that astronomy has been carried on for at least two thousand years but this is a time-interval very short compared with those that are met with in cosmology. In the model universe, the counterpart of human astronomers will be a single observer who will be defined as having the special world-line $r=0$. The observer will also be reckoned as making all his observations at the single instant t_0. In fig. 11, O represents the observer and the diagram also shows the

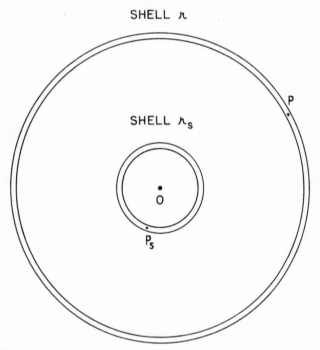

SHELL λ

SHELL λ_s

P

P_s

O

FIG. 11. Schematic shells centred at the observer.

cross-sections of two concentric spherical shells centred at O. Their thickness is small in each case and their inner radii are r_s and r respectively. In each shell there will be a number of particles of the representative gas having special world-lines.

These are, of course, the particles that represent the sources of radiation. Now consider a photon which is emitted from a source P in Shell r and a second photon, emitted from the source P_s in Shell r_s. Clearly, if these two photons are to arrive simultaneously at O, they must be emitted at times t and t_s, respectively, of which the former is an earlier instant than the latter. Moreover the photons from all sources in Shell r must leave at the instant t, if all are to be observed at O at the instant t_0; and similarly for all sources in Shell r_s. Instants such as t or t_s will be called 'departure-times'; they refer to the moments at which photons – or radiation generally – must leave the various shells in order to arrive at one and the same instant at O. The instant t_0 will be denoted the 'arrival-time' and the difference $t_0 - t$, the 'travel-time' for the radiation from Shell r.

An essential element in constructing the world-picture which the observer will obtain lies in the connection between the radial co-ordinate of a Shell and the departure-time. This is obtained from the path in space of the radiation and the speed with which it travels along the path. The former can be proved to be such that the angles θ, ϕ are constant along it. The speed is deduced from the null-geodesic principle which says that in space-time radiation moves so that $ds=0$ along the path. If in (1) $ds=0$, $d\theta=0$, $d\phi=0$, then the speed of the radiation in the reference frame (t, r, θ, ϕ) is

$$\frac{dr}{dt} = -\frac{c}{R}(1 + kr^2/4), \qquad (4)$$

the negative sign implying that the radiation is travelling toward $r=0$ from some greater value of r. The speed of the radiation relative to the reference frame (t, r, θ, ϕ) is clearly variable along the path since the right-hand side of the equation involves non-constant factors. The reader who has heard that in special relativity the velocity of light is constant need not be alarmed. Our reference frame is one in which the co-ordinates have been selected so as to be co-moving with the particles of the representative gas. But at any point on the path of the radiation local inertial reference frames of special relativity can be set up and relative to *these* the velocity of the radiation is always *c*. Like distance and time, speed or velocity in general relativity is not an absolute: its value depends on the reference frame relative to which it is measured.

Now consider a source in Shell r, the departure-time of the radiation being t and the arrival time at O being t_0. Then the equation (4) describes how long it takes the radiation to cover each infinitesimal piece of its path; to find the travel-time $t_0 - t$ needed to cover the whole interval r, the equation must be integrated. This operation gives

$$-\int_r^0 \frac{dr}{1 + kr^2/4} = c \int_t^{t_0} \frac{dt}{R(t)} . \tag{5}$$

which is the basic equation for the motion of radiation. It is a relation from which much can be deduced.

The first consequence concerns the red-shift of the spectral lines observed by O in the radiation reaching him from the source at the instant t_0. To find the amount of this red-shift it is easier to think of radiation as consisting of waves, rather than of photons. Each wave is associated with a brief time-interval, called its period. Suppose that the period at emission is dt, so that the source emits a wave between the instants t and $t + dt$. This wave eventually 'passes over' the observer between the instants t_0 and $t_0 + dt_0$ and its period* is therefore reckoned as being dt_0. The world-lines of source and observer being special ones, the upper and lower limits in the integral

* The assumption that source and observer have special world-lines implies that the periods dt and dt_0 are respectively equal to the invariant intervals ds and ds_0.

on the left-hand side of (5) are unchanged whether this equation refers to the 'head' or the 'tail' of the light wave. It follows that

$$\int_{t+td}^{t_0+dt_0} \frac{dt}{R(t)} = \int_t^{t_0} \frac{dt}{R(t)},$$

and the rules of the calculus then show that

$$\frac{dt}{R(t)} = \frac{dt_0}{R(t_0)}. \tag{6}$$

Thus dt and dt_0 are equal only if R has the same value at the departure- and the arrival-time. But this will only happen if source and observer are at relative rest. Thus, if they are in relative motion, the period of the wave when it reaches the observer will be different from its period at emission. The displacement of the spectral lines thus theoretically predicted is deduced from the last formula by saying that the emitted wavelength is $\lambda = c \, dt$ and that the received is $\lambda + d\lambda = c \, dt_0$. Hence the displacement δ ($= d\lambda/\lambda$) is

$$\delta = \frac{R(t_0)}{R(t)} - 1 = \frac{R_0}{R} - 1. \tag{7}$$

This formula holds for all sources in Shell r having special world-lines and for radio waves as well as for light waves.

When a particular model universe is given, it is possible, because R is then a known function of t and k has been assigned one of its three permissible values, to express δ in terms of the travel-time, or conversely, by an exact formula that also contains the arrival-time. For example, the relation in Milne's model is

$$t_0 - t = t_0 \delta/(1 + \delta).$$

But for the general model, because R is still unspecified as a particular function of t and k has not yet been chosen, the best that can be done is to work out δ as an infinite series in the travel-time of which the first two terms are

$$\delta = \frac{R_0'}{R_0}(t_0 - t) + \tfrac{1}{2} \left\{ 2\left(\frac{R_0'}{R_0}\right)^2 - \frac{R_0''}{R_0} \right\} (t_0 - t)^2 + - - -. \quad (8)$$

Here a suffix zero denotes that the function in question is evaluated at the instant t_0. The two functions of the arrival-time that occur in the last formula, namely,

$$h_1 = R_0'/R_0, \quad h_2 = R_0''/R_0, \quad (9)$$

are very important in cosmology and will be called respectively the *Hubble parameter* and the *acceleration parameter*. They also occur in the series which expresses the value of the scale-factor at time t in terms of the travel-time, namely,

$$R(t) = R_0 \left\{ 1 - h_1(t_0 - t) + \tfrac{1}{2}h_2(t_0 - t)^2 + - - - \right\}. \quad (10)$$

Before proceeding with the discussion of the parameters two important considerations must be noticed. The first is that the spectral line displacement δ will be a red-shift only if the value of the scale-factor at the arrival-time is greater than its value at the departure-time for sources in all shells. Or at least, for all those shells whose sources emit radiation strong enough to be recordable when it reaches the observer. This means that R must be an increasing function of the time over the time interval corresponding to the travel-time of the radiation from the most remote recordable sources. The theory of the model universe does not guarantee that this must be so; in other words, a uniform motion of contraction of the representative gas is as much a possibility as is an expansion. Of these two alternatives the one that corresponds to the observed universe can be selected only by an appeal to observation. Since the observed shift of the spectral lines of galaxies is toward the red, the case of an increasing scale-factor will be adopted and it will hereafter be taken for granted that the displacement given by either (7) or (8) is the quantity which, in the model universe, represents the observed red-shift.

The second point concerns the way in which the observer will record any physical characteristic of the sources that possesses the U-property. Suppose that T denotes this characteristic; then for a source in Shell r, the value of T is $T(t)$ whereas for a source in Shell r_s it will be $T(t_s)$. These two values of T will in general be different. But now equation (7) provides a means of replacing the departure-time of the radiation by the red-shift for the source in question. In the observer's world-picture, characteristics possessing the U-property will therefore appear to vary with the red-shift. His picture will indeed be a composite one containing extracts, so to speak, of the state of affairs in the model universe at successive instants of past time. The net result will usually be a world-picture that is non-uniform and quite different from that of a super-human being who could see the entire universe at a single instant t. This being, of course, has the advantage over the human astronomer in that he does not need to wait for electromagnetic energy, travelling at a finite speed, to bring him information.

We return now to the Hubble parameter and the acceleration parameter, the first of which is proportional to the velocity of sources close to the observer at the instant t_0, divided by the scale-factor at that same instant. The second is similarly related to the acceleration of the nearby sources. The Hubble parameter is usually called the Hubble constant, a name which unfortunately prejudges one of the most interesting questions in cosmology, namely, do the galaxies in fact move in such a fashion that the Hubble parameter is a constant of nature? Once again the theory of relativity which we are using gives no answer to this question: it must be found by an appeal to observation.

As they have been defined in the equations above, the Hubble parameter is expressed as the reciprocal of a time, the acceleration parameter, as the square of the reciprocal of a time. Hence the ratio of h_2 to $h_1{}^2$ must be a pure number, the *acceleration factor*, which it is convenient to write as

$$q_0 = -h_2/h_1{}^2. \tag{11}$$

This means that a positive acceleration corresponds to a negative value of q_0 whereas a negative acceleration – a retardation – corresponds to a positive q_0.

Instead of stating the Hubble parameter as the reciprocal of a time, an alternative mode of expression has come into use. The time $1/h_1$, in seconds, is divided into one kilometre to give a quantity u which is therefore a velocity in km/sec. Symbolically,

$$u \text{ km/sec} = 1 \text{ km} \times (h_1 \text{ sec}^{-1}).$$

But since the Hubble parameter is essentially the reciprocal of a time, the arbitrarily introduced kilometre must be removed again so that

$$h_1 \text{ sec}^{-1} = u \text{ km/sec} \div 1 \text{ km}. \tag{12}$$

Note however that 1 km is 1 mpc divided by $3 \cdot 087 \times 10^{19}$. Hence we can obtain a quantity H expressed in km/sec/mpc by writing in place of (12)

$$H = \frac{(u \text{ km/sec}) \times 3 \cdot 087 \times 10^{19}}{1 \text{ mpc}}$$
$$= 3 \cdot 087 \times 10^{19} \, h_1 \text{ km/sec/mpc}. \tag{13}$$

When the time unit is the second, the numerical values of h_1 and h_2 will be very small compared with unity. On the other hand, the numbers expressing H are of modest size and there is therefore an advantage of convenience in using H instead of h_1. But there is a disadvantage also; we may jump to the conclusion that u is necessarily the velocity of recession of the galaxies corresponding to the red-shift. But this is moving too fast: we have not yet defined what distance means in the model universe. And velocity, if this term means anything at all, must mean the rate of change of some distance with respect to some time. To these questions we must now briefly turn.

Definitions of Distance

So far no definition has been given of what is meant by spatial distance in a model universe. Various suggestions have been put forward by different people: for example, it has been argued [34] that the only 'natural measure of spatial distance offered by the general model' is the quantity that appears on the left-hand side of equation (5) multiplied by R_0. It is not explained, however, what 'natural' means in this statement; it is clearly not intended to imply 'imposed by nature' and no operational procedure is known by which this distance could be directly measured. Moreover the choice of R_0, rather than some other value of R, is quite arbitrary. Indeed, we have here an example of the difficulty inherent in defining distance by purely theoretical means; the definition remains arbitrary and the adjective 'natural' really means 'mathematically the most obvious'. If we are not to lose ourselves in a plethora of imaginable distances, it is necessary to reconstruct in the model universe a distance which is closely tied to a measuring procedure that astronomers on earth can in fact carry out. It has already been remarked that the principal criterion of distance in the case of a galaxy is its apparent magnitude, and the distance associated with measurements of luminosities is luminosity-distance. To the development of this idea in the model universe we now turn.

Looking back to the classical theory by which equations (3) and (4) of Chapter 2 were established, we may state the problem of finding the luminosity-distance D of a source of radiation of intrinsic power-output P located in Shell r as follows: D must be a combination of the co-ordinates of the source such that the intensity of the source, as it would be measured by the observer at O, shall be proportional to P/D^2. The luminosity-distance must be independent of the physical characteristics that control the emission of radiation by the source; it must, for example, apply equally well to the

H

optical brightness of the source and to its intensity as meaured by any radio waves it emits. Thus D is presumably a function of r and of the departure- and arrival-times, t and t_0 of the radiation.

A simple way of identifying D in the model universe is to regard radiation as consisting of photons and to consider monochromatic radiation in the first instance. Let the source emit photons of frequency f_e, each photon therefore having an energy hf_e where h is Planck's constant. The following results can then be proved, though proofs will not be given here. Firstly, a photon emitted from a source in Shell r with frequency f_e is received at O with frequency $f=f_e/(1+\delta)$ because of the red-shift. The increase of wavelength from λ_e to $\lambda=\lambda_e(1+\delta)$ has to be compensated for by a decrease of frequency to maintain the equalities $\lambda f=\lambda_e f_e=c$. Thus the energy at emission of the photon, hf_e, becomes $hf=hf_e/(1+\delta)$ at receipt and therefore the received energy per photon is decreased. Secondly, if the source emits photons uniformly in all directions at the rate n_e per second, the corresponding rate of arrival at the observer is reduced by the red-shift to $n=n_e/(1+\delta)$. Thirdly, the observer will be moving away from the photon advancing toward him, during the photon's journey. Therefore the unit area on which the radiation energy is received will diminish in angular size – from the photon's point of view! – during the travel-time of the radiation. Following out the consequences of these ideas, one can show that the observed brightness of the source, which is the rate of arrival of electromagnetic energy on a unit area held by the observer perpendicular to the direction in which he sees the source, would be

$$\frac{h f_e n_e}{4\pi D^2},$$ (14)

where

$$D=\frac{R_0{}^2}{R}\ \frac{r}{1+kr^2/4}=R_0(1+\delta)\frac{r}{1+kr^2/4}, \qquad (15)$$

and this is the luminosity-distance* of the source in Shell r. The expression contains both the red-shift and the r-co-ordinate of the source, but the latter can be expressed, in theory at least, in terms of the red-shift through equations (5) and (7) above. For the general model, the result is an infinite series for D in terms of δ, of which the first two terms are

$$D=\frac{c\delta}{h_1}\left\{1+\tfrac{1}{2}(1-q_0)\delta+---\right\}. \qquad (16)$$

This method of finding the luminosity-distance really gives the way in which the intensity of a source of power-output $hf_e n_e$ would vary for observers at different luminosity-distances from it. This is not quite what is wanted: the observer O of fig. 11 wants to compare the intensities of similar sources of radiation at different distances from himself. Moreover, the photonic number n_e is rarely known for each frequency emitted by natural sources. Their radiation is usually described in terms of waves carrying energy. A relatively simple illustration of the way in which these points are taken into account is provided by Class II radio sources. Their output of energy at each frequency is proportional to a power x of the frequency. Thus a source in Shell r emits in the range f_e to f_e+df_e an amount of energy per second equal to $C f_e{}^x df_e$, where C is some constant. On reaching the observer, the frequency and the frequency interval have each been reduced in the ratio $1:(1+\delta)$ because of the red-shift and have become f and df respectively. Thus the amount of energy

---

* This is the definition of luminosity-distance adopted by most investigators[35]. Bondi [36] modifies it by omitting the factor $(1+\delta)$ in (15). He believes that $hf_e n_e$ ought to be divided by $(1+\delta)^2$ before the luminosity-distance is identified.

passing perpendicularly through unit area per second at the observer is

$$\frac{C(1+\delta)^{1+x} f^x \, df}{4\pi D^2}.$$

But the radio telescope records only a fraction $\sigma(f)$ of this quantity and therefore the flux-density of the source in Shell r is registered by the observer as

$$S = \frac{C(1+\delta)^{1+x} \sigma(f) f^x}{4\pi D^2}.$$

A similar standard source in Shell r_s of fig. 11 may be defined to be one with the same value of the spectral index and the same value of C. The observer's radio telescope also operates at frequency f and over the frequency-interval df for the standard source. Hence denoting by the suffix s quantities which refer to the standard source, we have

$$\frac{S}{S_s} = \left(\frac{1+\delta}{1+\delta_s}\right)^{1+x} \frac{D_s^2}{D^2},$$

which can also be written as

$$\frac{D}{D_s} = \left(\frac{1+\delta}{1+\delta_s}\right)^{\frac{1+x}{2}} \left(\frac{S_s}{S}\right)^{\frac{1}{2}}. \tag{17}$$

It is interesting to compare this ratio of luminosity-distances with that of local distances given by equation (3) of Chapter 2, which implied that the sources were at rest in a Euclidean space. The comparison reveals that, when $x = -1$, the ratio of luminosity-distances is equal to that of local distances for the same S and S_s. Hence for this particular value of the spectral index, the luminosity-distances of a set of Class II radio sources in motion would mimic their local distances calculated as if the sources were at rest. This is an example of a more general principle, namely, that the nature of the spectral energy-curve for a source of radiation can affect the relationship between the luminosity-distance and the measured intensity of the source.

This principle has a bearing on the luminosity of an optical source. The power emitted in the frequency interval f_e to $f_e + df_e$ by a source in Shell r is $P(f_e)df_e$ and the function P is no longer a simple one, as the curve I of fig. 10 indicates. To take account of as much complication as possible, it may also be assumed that the function P possesses the U-property, so that, from the observer's point of view, it will not only involve the emission frequency f_e, but the red-shift of the source as well. The working out of these effects would lead to mathematics beyond the scope of this book. Suffice it to say that a luminosity analogous to L in equation (4) of Chapter 2 can be defined, that the ratio of apparent magnitudes is still defined by equation (6) of the same chapter and that the standard source may be replaced by the absolute magnitude of the given source, provided that precautions are taken. These are that the source when placed at 10 pc has the same function P as in its actual position and that the red-shift is zero because of its propinquity to the observer. In place of the equation (8) of Chapter 2 for the local distance, it then turns out that we have

$$\log D = 0.2 \{m - (K_1 + W_1)\delta - M\} + 1, \qquad (18)$$

where K_1 and W_1 are constants. The formula ignores terms in the red-shift that involve the square and higher powers of this quantity. The effect of the K-correction term, $K_1\delta$, is to rectify the distorted curve II of fig. 10 and to bring it into coincidence with curve I. The term $W_1\delta$ is present only when P does in fact possess the U-property. It is possible, but not necessary, to regard the K-correction as modifying the observed apparent magnitude m of the source and to introduce an apparent magnitude 'corrected for red-shift', $m_c = m - K_1\delta$. In the same way the term $W_1\delta$, which implies that there are secular variations in the emission properties of the sources, may be regarded as a 'correction' to the absolute magnitude. The source in its actual position in Shell r would then have absolute magnitude $M + W_1 \delta$, but when transported in our imagination to 10 pc, its absolute magnitude would be M.

In conclusion, still another kind of operationally definable distance may be mentioned. Suppose that the sources of radiation in all Shells of fig. 11 have the same small linear diameter. Then the angular diameter of a source, as it is measured by the observer, is the angle made at his eye by the null-geodesics, one of which starts from one end of a cross-section of the source and the second, from the opposite end. The angle is really fixed the moment the radiation leaves the source, i.e. by the departure-time. If the 'distance by apparent size' of any one of the sources is defined as in classical physics by the ratio of the linear diameter of the source to its angular diameter as measured by the observer, it can be proved that this kind of distance is

$$\xi = R(t)\frac{r}{1 + kr^2/4} = \frac{D}{(1 + \delta)^2} . \tag{19}$$

This makes it obvious that the distance by apparent size and the luminosity-distance of the same source are only equal if the red-shift is negligibly small compared with unity. If however the red-shift is as large as 0·4, then the distance by apparent size is only 51 per cent of the luminosity-distance. Such differences need surprise us only if we still cling to the notion inherent in classical physics that there is an absolute or 'true' distance. Relativity theory substitutes for this idea the notion of distances related to specific operations of measurement.

Doppler Formulae and the Velocity of Recession

In Chapter 2 it was stated that classical physics predicted that the velocity corresponding to a given red-shift was simply the magnitude of the red-shift multiplied by the velocity of light. The familiarity of this result has led many scientists to treat it as a law of nature rather than as one of the consequences of a particular theory about nature. The model universes with which cosmology deals are based on a different theory and they entail new Doppler formulae. To see this it is easiest, in the first instance, to consider Milne's model whose specifications are $R(t) = ct$ and $k = -1$. The integrations involved in equation (5) can therefore now be carried out and indeed exact expressions for the luminosity-distance and the distance by apparent size in terms of the red-shift can also be obtained.* Moreover in this model the Hubble parameter h_1 has the value $1/t_0$ whereas the acceleration parameter is zero.

How then can the observer define the velocity of a source of radiation in Milne's model? A conceivable procedure would be to measure the luminosity-distance at the instant t_0, wait a brief while and measure it again at the instant $t_0 + dt_0$. The difference in the values of the luminosity-distances divided by the time-interval dt_0 would give a velocity, which may be denoted symbolically by V_D. A detailed calculation shows that

$$V_D = \frac{D}{t_0} = c\delta(1 + \tfrac{1}{2}\delta).$$

A second imaginable procedure would be to measure the distance by apparent size at each of the two instants. A velocity, denoted by V_ξ, would then be obtained by dividing the difference of the distances by apparent size by the time-interval dt_0 and it can be proved that

$$V_\xi = \frac{\xi}{t_0} = c\delta(1 + \tfrac{1}{2}\delta)(1 + \delta)^{-2}.$$

A third possibility is the one which Milne himself adopted.

* The formulae are $D = ct_0\delta (1 + \tfrac{1}{2}\delta)$, $\xi = ct_0\delta (1 + \tfrac{1}{2}\delta) (1 + \delta)^{-2}$.

Let the observer's clock read time t and let him send out a burst of radiation towards the source at time t'_0, which returns to him at time t_0. Then the radar distance which the observer assigns to the source at the instant t_0 is $\frac{1}{2}c(t_0 - t'_0)$. Incidentally it is an interesting property of Milne's model that this radar distance happens to be identical with distance by apparent size. Now Milne defines the velocity of the source as its radar distance divided by the average, $\frac{1}{2}(t'_0 + t_0)$, of the instants of emission and return of the signal made by observer. Let V_m be this velocity and let δ be the red-shift which the observer detects in the light from the source at the instant t_0. It can then be proved that V_m is related to the red-shift δ through the Doppler formula of special relativity, namely,

$$1 + \delta = \left(\frac{1 + V_m/c}{1 - V_m/c} \right)^{1/2} .$$

The last three formulae show that a variety of Doppler formulae are possible in Milne's model and that none of them coincides with that of classical physics.* These differences arise partly because the definitions of distance are themselves different in each case and also because, for the third one, a peculiar definition of the time-interval by which the distance is to be divided was adopted. Unfortunately however all three measuring procedures constitute science-fiction experiments: no astronomer would expect to get differences in the distances unless he measured them at intervals of many million years. To say this is to say that the experiment is one which astrono-

* For example, if the red-shift is equal to 0·4, the classical velocity of recession would be 0·4c. But the three formulae give, respectively, $V_D = 0·48c$, $V_\xi = 0·245c$, $V_m = 0·324c$ for the same red-shift. Note also that $V_D = c$ for $\delta = 0·73$, $V_m = c$ only for an infinite value of δ and that there is no real value of δ which makes $V_\xi = c$. There is therefore no unambiguous way of asserting that source and observer have a relative velocity equal to the local velocity of light.

mers cannot in fact perform. Therefore velocities of recession are theoretical constructs built up out of observables such as the red-shift, the apparent luminosity of a source of radiation or its angular diameter.

In Milne's model it can be proved that the three velocities V_D, V_ξ, and V_m all reduce to $c\delta$ for sources of radiation so close to the observer that their red-shifts are very small compared with unity. Therefore, under these circumstances, the velocities degenerate to the velocity v of the classical Doppler formula (2) of Chapter 2. Another important property of V_D and V_ξ is that each is always proportional to its corresponding distance and that the constant of proportionality is the Hubble parameter h_1.

For the general model (1), it has been possible to work out the analogues of the velocities that are the rates of change of luminosity-distance and of distance by apparent size. As is to be expected, the results are very much more complicated than in Milne's model and will not be given here. The property that a velocity is equal to the Hubble parameter times the corresponding distance is now only true *provided that the red-shift of the source is small*; for larger red-shifts the relationship is non-linear and its exact nature is determined by the specific function R and the value of k for the model. For small red-shifts, it is still true that all velocities reduce to the classical Doppler velocity $c\delta$. These general conclusions regarding sources which are close to the observer permit us to give an interpretation to the velocity u which was manufactured in equation (12). Since, for these nearby sources, the Hubble parameter is velocity divided by distance, however these quantities may be defined, it follows that u must be the velocity of recession of nearby sources. Moreover, since any velocity reduces to $c\delta$ for small red-shifts, u must also be the classical Doppler velocity. But as soon as red-shifts of any size are in question, such as those that are measured in the spectra of the fainter clusters of galaxies, all these statements cease to be true. The velocity u then simply becomes an indirect way of describing the Hubble parameter.

The reader may well be pardoned if he finds this account of the velocity of recession of the galaxies confusing; he has probably read categorical statements to the effect that the velocity of recession is proportional to the distance of a galaxy or that if a galaxy had a red-shift equal to unity, its velocity would equal that of light, and so on. What is invariably omitted from such statements is the qualifying clause: 'provided that distance means so and so' in the first statement and 'provided that the lessons of special relativity are ignored' in the second. The upshot of our investigations on distances and velocities of recession in model universes is that both concepts must, if possible, be avoided. There is far too much ambiguity connected with them and far too much need for qualifications whenever they are mentioned. These complications do not exist with respect to the observable quantities involved, such as the red-shift, the apparent magnitude of a galaxy or the flux-density of a radio source. Our further discussions will therefore be carried out in terms of observables, in so far as the theory permits of this being done.

Chapter 6

SELECTING A MODEL UNIVERSE

We are now in possession of a sufficient amount of theory to approach the central problem that must engage our attention, which is, does astronomical observation provide data that will enable us to identify the model universe which best represents the state of affairs in the observed universe? It will be our contention that the red-shift supplies this information in part, if not completely. A complete answer would imply that the scale-factor would be known as an explicit function of the time and the space-curvature constant would also be uniquely selected. The red-shift data are at present only accurate and extensive enough, as we shall see, to reject certain wide classes of functions that the scale-factor might be; they do not pin-point some particular function among the remaining eligible competitors. To determine the space-curvature constant it will be necessary to supplement the red-shift data by an estimate of the average density of matter in the observed universe.

Red-shifts of Clusters of Galaxies

The start that can thus be made in the determination of the scale-factor consists in seeking the numerical value of the Hubble parameter and of the acceleration parameter or, in place of the latter, the acceleration factor which was defined in equation (11), Chapter 5. The method employed is common to general relativity, kinematical relativity and the steady-state theory with this difference however. In general relativity it is used to select the model universe; in the other

123

two theories it purports to verify that a pre-selected model does in fact fit the observed universe. This method consists of using simultaneously the two formulae which have been developed for the luminosity-distance. The first of these is equation (16) of Chapter 5 which expresses the luminosity-distance in terms of the red-shift and the two parameters. It is truncated at its second term on the right-hand side and it therefore reads

$$D = \frac{c\delta}{h_1} \left\{ 1 + \tfrac{1}{2} (1 - q_0) \, \delta \right\} .$$

This approximation, of course, implies that all subsequent results will be valid only up to red-shifts of modest size, for example, when δ does not exceed 0·2 or 0·3. The second formula is equation (18), Chapter 5, wherein the luminosity-distance is expressed in terms of apparent magnitude, absolute magnitude and the red-shift. This formula is, as has already been mentioned, an approximate one in the red-shift and it is assumed that the degree of approximation is the same as in the truncated form of equation (16). Since both formulae involve the luminosity-distance, this variable can be eliminated and a direct relationship* obtained between the two observable quantities, the red-shift δ of a source of radiation on the one hand and its apparent magnitude m on the other. It turns out mathematically that the simplest way of expressing the relationship between δ and m is to use certain combinations of these quantities. One of these is $y = m - 5 \log c\delta$ and then the relationship turns out to be

$$y = A + B\delta \tag{1}$$

where the constants A and B are defined by

$$\left. \begin{array}{l} A = M - 5 - 5 \log h_1, \\ B = 1\cdot086 + K_1 + W_1 - 1\cdot086 q_0. \end{array} \right\} \tag{2}$$

* The complete equation is
$m = 5 \log c\delta + (1\cdot086 + K_1 + W_1 - 1\cdot086 q_0)\delta + (M - 5 - 5 \log h_1)$.

Hence the graph of y against δ will be a straight line of which the slope is equal to B; the constant A corresponds to the value of y for sources with very small (theoretically zero) red-shifts. A second combination of m and δ which is also employed is the following: the observed apparent magnitude m is first corrected by means of the K-correction so that it becomes $m_c = m - K_1\delta$. Then the combination $z = m_c - 5$ log $c\delta$ is set up and the formula mathematically equivalent to (1) is

$$z = A + B'\delta. \qquad (3)$$

Here A has the same meaning as in (2) and $B' = B - K_1$ because the K-correction has been incorporated into z.

The next step is to find a set of objects whose apparent magnitudes and red-shifts have been observed and to see whether the corresponding y or z is a linear function of the red-shift. They must be objects whose intrinsic luminosities can be regarded as being equal to one another because the apparent magnitudes will then provide an index of the distances of the objects. The red-shifts should also extend to as large a value as possible, so that remote objects are being considered. All these conditions are best satisfied by clusters of galaxies, in particular by the eighteen studied by Humason, Mayall and Sandage [21] to which reference has already been made in Chapter 3. Their synthetic brightest members may be assumed to have the same absolute magnitude. The apparent magnitudes for the fainter clusters have been measured by Sandage using photographic means. The details for these eighteen clusters will be found in Table A of the Appendix. The apparent magnitude shown is that of the synthetic brightest member galaxy of the cluster and the red-shift is that for the cluster as a whole. A plot of y against δ is shown in fig. 12; across the top of the figure the cluster members are shown, together with an arrow, to indicate which point refers to which cluster. In our subsequent discussion it will be con-

126

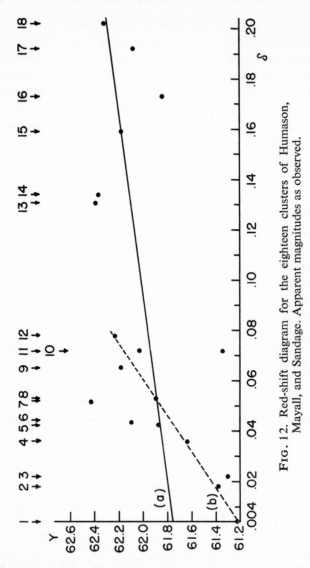

FIG. 12. Red-shift diagram for the eighteen clusters of Humason, Mayall, and Sandage. Apparent magnitudes as observed.

venient to speak of a cluster point being 'moved vertically' when it is displaced parallel to the axis of y. If a cluster point is moved vertically upwards the red-shift is not altered but the number expressing the apparent magnitude of the synthetic brightest cluster member is increased, because y and m increase together. Thus moving a cluster point vertically upwards is tantamount to reducing the apparent brightness of the synthetic brightest cluster member, making it fainter than it is in fact observed to be. Contrariwise, moving a cluster point vertically downwards implies an increase of brightness.

It is believed that the red-shifts are much more accurately measured than are the apparent magnitudes.* Hence in a diagram such as that of fig. 12, the red-shifts may be regarded as fixed and any changes in the positions of the points are vertical ones due to alterations of opinion about the apparent magnitudes.

An unfortunate feature of fig. 12 is the wide gap that contains no cluster points. It lies in the range $\delta=0\cdot078$ to $\delta=0\cdot131$. To the left of the gap, lie the points for twelve clusters and here y seems to increase rapidly with the red-shift. To the right of the gap, lie the cluster points for six clusters whose synthetic brightest members have apparent magnitude $17\cdot92$ or fainter. The relatively rapid increase of y with δ noted for the first twelve points, has now apparently come to a halt. The straight line that lies evenly among all the eighteen points has the equation

$$y=61\cdot74+2\cdot8\delta \tag{4}$$

and it is marked (a) in fig. 12. Hence we now have values for the constants A and B of equation (1). But on examining the definition of A in equation (2), it is clear that this constant by itself fails to give the Hubble parameter: the value of the

* The error in δ probably does not exceed $\pm0\cdot0003$. Such an error would move cluster point 1 vertically up or down by $0\cdot2$ units; but by the time cluster point 3 is reached the movement is reduced to $0\cdot03$ and is thereafter far smaller.

absolute magnitude M of the synthetic brightest member of a cluster must also be known. In Chapter 2 it was indicated that the intrinsically most luminous galaxies in our neighbourhood probably had absolute magnitudes in the range $-19 \cdot 9$ to $-20 \cdot 9$. For lack of any alternative, it will be assumed that the synthetic brightest cluster member has an absolute magnitude lying in this range also. Using this datum combined with $A = 61 \cdot 74$, it turns out that the Hubble parameter H lies between 103 and 163 km/sec/mpc. Similar considerations apply to the calculation of the acceleration factor from a given value of B: the constants K_1 and W_1 must also be independently known. The first one is deducible from Sandage's K-correction and it turns out that $K_1 = 4 \cdot 7$; the second one is much more difficult to estimate, for it would depend on the way in which the evolution of a cluster of galaxies would affect the intrinsic luminosities of the brightest cluster members. At present there does not appear to be any direct observational evidence which indicates a value of W_1 different from zero. It used to be thought that elliptical galaxies exhibited a systematic difference of colour that depended on distance. But this effect was eventually shown to be due to an error in the interpretation of the data. Recent work by Morgan and Mayall on the spectra of galaxies shows that there is a correlation between spectrum and type of galaxy. There is no indication that the nature of the spectrum varies systematically with distance. Thus estimates of W_1 are based on evolutionary theory; a computation by Sandage [21] suggests a zero value for the photographic magnitudes which we are employing. Thus for the moment W_1 will be assigned a zero value, though this point will be discussed again in the next section. Introducing then $B = 2 \cdot 8$, $K_1 = 4 \cdot 7$ and $W_1 = 0$ into the second of the equations (2), it follows that the acceleration factor q_0 has the positive value $2 \cdot 7$. It will be remembered that a positive acceleration factor means that there is a retardation present. Therefore the interpretation of the diagram of fig. 12 by means of the line (a) leads to the conclusion that the expansion of the model universe is being retarded at the present moment and that the Hubble parameter, which gives the present rate of expansion, may be estimated to lie somewhere in the range 100 to 160 km/sec/mpc.

It is obviously necessary to marshal as much evidence as possible for or against this conclusion. Looking at fig. 12 again, we could decide to ignore the six points to the right of the gap and to draw the best fitting straight line through the twelve left-hand points. It is shown as the dotted line (b) whose equation is $y = 61\cdot17 + 13\cdot7\delta$. Proceeding with the calculation of the Hubble parameter and acceleration factor as was done for line (a), it turns out that H now lies in the range 134 to 212 km/sec/mpc so that the present rate of expansion has been increased. But the principal change is in q_0, whose value is now found to be $-7\cdot2$. This negative value implies that the expansion of the model universe is proceeding at an ever more rapid rate at the present moment; a conclusion opposite to that deduced from line (a). It is not, of course, argued that there is any justification for ignoring the six right-hand cluster points in fig. 12. Obviously they correspond to the largest red-shifts, where the effects of the expansion are most conspicuous. The line (b) is mentioned to show that, if the six right-hand cluster points could be moved vertically upwards through something like a magnitude or two, the conclusion regarding the retardation of the expansion would be destroyed. But to do this, it would be necessary to find evidence that the apparent magnitudes measured by Sandage for the faint clusters had been grossly overestimated. We shall return to this point presently.

It may be objected that the corrected apparent magnitudes m_c should have been used in place of the observed magnitudes

I

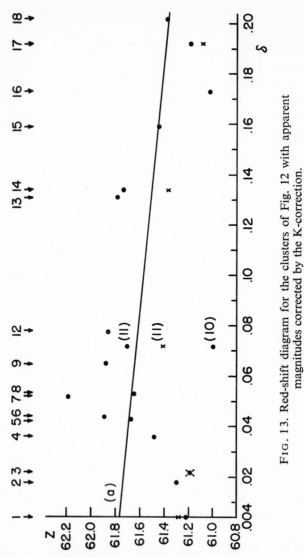

FIG. 13. Red-shift diagram for the clusters of Fig. 12 with apparent magnitudes corrected by the K-correction.

m. In fig. 13, therefore, is shown a plot of *z* against δ for the same eighteen clusters. The diagram also contains certain additional points that are marked by crosses. Their significance will emerge presently; for the moment they can be ignored. The best fitting straight line is marked (a) and has the equation $z = 61 \cdot 77 - 2 \cdot 0 \delta$. The deduced range for H is now 101 to 160 km/sec/mpc and so differs in no significant way from the value obtained from line (a) of fig. 12. Since we now have $B' = -2 \cdot 0$ and $B' \simeq 1 \cdot 1 - 1 \cdot 1 \; q_0$, it follows that $q_0 = 2 \cdot 8$ and again there is no essential alteration from the fig. 12 result. It may therefore be concluded that the use of the corrected apparent magnitudes m_c, as opposed to the uncorrected, makes no difference in the present connection.

In Abell's work on clusters of galaxies [20], there is found a group of eighteen, seven of which do not occur in the Humason, Mayall and Sandage investigation.* The photo-red apparent magnitude† of the tenth brightest cluster member has been roughly estimated by Abell, and the red-shifts for these clusters have been measured. The K-correction for photo-red magnitudes is of the second order in the red-shift and can be ignored for the present purpose. Fig. 14 shows a plot of z, calculated using Abell's magnitudes, against δ. The scatter of the points is now so great that only the mean line, parallel to the δ-axis, can be legitimately drawn through them. This is a line of zero slope, for which therefore $B' = 0$. This implies that $q_0 = 1$, assuming again that $W_1 = 0$. Thus the retardation is still present, but the acceleration factor has been reduced compared with the result drawn from figs. 12 and 13. The conclusion suggested by this group of clusters is that rough approximations to apparent magnitudes will lead to a decrease in the value of the acceleration factor in the direction

---

* See Table B of Appendix, in which the new clusters are numbered 19 to 25.

† The magnitude as it would be measured on the plates of the Sky Atlas that were sensitive to red, rather than to blue, light.

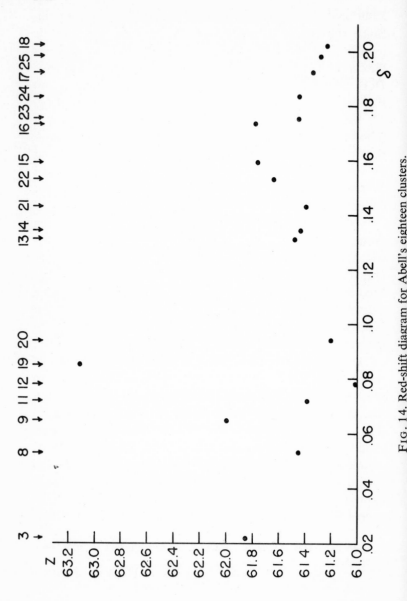

FIG. 14. Red-shift diagram for Abell's eighteen clusters.

which would turn a retardation of the expansion into an acceleration.

Lastly there are data due to Baum [37] on clusters 1, 3, 11, 14, and 17 and also on three clusters 26, 27, 28 (see Table C of Appendix). Full details of these measurements have not been published, but they consist of photoelectric observations of some of the brightest galaxies in the clusters, which produce spectral energy-curves similar to curve II of fig. 10. The red-shifts of the five clusters, Nos 1 to 17, are known from photographic spectroscopy; this is also true for cluster 28 whose red-shift is that obtained spectroscopically by Minkowski [37]. Thus, for these six clusters, the photoelectric method may be employed to estimate roughly the corrected apparent magnitude of the synthetic brightest cluster member. But for clusters 26 and 27, Baum has to deduce from his spectral energy-curves both the red-shift and the corrected apparent magnitude. At the Mexico City meeting of the American Astronomical Society in August 1960, a graph of Baum's results was exhibited. From this graph, the author of this book has read off the red-shifts and corrected apparent

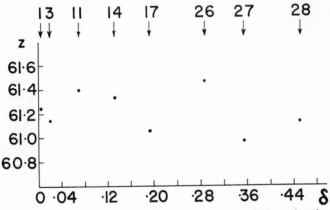

FIG. 15. Red-shift diagram for eight clusters observed photoelectrically by Baum.

magnitudes listed in Table C of the Appendix. The consequential values of z are plotted against δ in fig. 15. The number of points being small, and their scatter wide, prudence suggests that they should be represented by the mean line parallel to the δ-axis. Such a line yields once more a value of the acceleration factor equal to $+1$, a conclusion also drawn by Baum. However, Baum's apparent magnitudes can hardly be accurate to less than an error of $\pm0\cdot5$. Therefore one may speculate, on comparing figs. 14 and 15, that the $+1$ value of the acceleration factor may arise, in part at least, from the roughness in the measurement of the apparent magnitudes.

Before drawing final conclusions for this section, it is necessary to notice the criticisms which have been made against this kind of investigation.

Criticisms and Conclusions

The criticisms are levelled essentially against the retardation of the expansion, rather than at the value of the Hubble parameter. The three main objections are, firstly, that the apparent magnitudes used in figs. 12 and 13 are untrustworthy; secondly, that the clusters are not really comparable with each other; and thirdly, that it is illegitimate to assume that W_1 is zero. These objections are relevant only in so far as they can lead to substantial changes in the positions of the cluster points in figs. 12 or 13. Thus it may readily be conceded that the apparent magnitudes may be in error, one way or the other, by two or three tenths of a magnitude without affecting our results. As has already been pointed out, it would be necessary to move the right-hand six cluster points vertically upwards through distances of the order of one or two magnitudes (i.e. one or two units on the scale of z) to reverse the sign of the acceleration in any convincing fashion. Statements have been made that Sandage's magnitudes are on the whole too bright and that they also contain systematic errors. Such

remarks would constitute valid criticisms if his magnitudes
had been remeasured and the amount of the error had been
indicated. In an attempt to estimate the errors, Baum's
points for clusters 1, 3, 11, 14 and 17 have been transferred
from fig. 15 to fig. 13 and are shown by crosses. The transfer
was calibrated by taking cluster point 3 (Coma) to be identical
in both diagrams. This means that the values of z listed in
Table C of the Appendix must all be increased by 0·04 so as
to make the z-entries for cluster 3 equal in Tables A and C.
It then follows that Sandage's magnitudes for clusters 1 and 3
are essentially the same as Baum's but, for clusters 11, 14 and
17, the Sandage magnitudes must be *fainter* than Baum's
because the crosses fall below the original points in each case.
The representation of the points in fig. 15 by a straight line
parallel to the δ-axis is also perhaps now explicable. If in
fig. 13, the cluster points for clusters 1, 3, 11, 14 and 17,
calculated from Sandage's magnitudes, had alone been present, the paucity of points would have compelled a representation by a straight line parallel to the δ-axis. It is the
larger number of points actually found on fig. 13 which
seems to be responsible for the downward slope from left to
right of line (a). This slope makes q_0 more nearly equal to 3
than to Baum's value of unity.

Cluster 28 is a very important one because its red-shift is
very large and also because there is independent spectro-
scopic evidence of the amount of the red-shift. Corrected by
the addition of 0·04 so as to make it comparable with the
entries of Table A, the z-value for this cluster is 61·10. But
now the value of z predicted by line (a) of fig. 13 at a red-shift
of 0·46 is $z = 61.77 - 2(0.46) = 60.85$. Comparing with 61·10,
we see that, if Baum's apparent magnitude for cluster 28 were
reduced by 0·25, agreement would result. But Baum's magnitudes very probably contain errors at least as large as this.
Hence, whatever may be the case for the other seven clusters

of Table C, it is not possible to argue that line (a) of fig. 13 fails to represent cluster 28 also.

Suppose however that we decide to consider Sandage's magnitudes to be as roughly estimated as are Abell's photo-red magnitudes. Then we would not be justified in representing the points in figs. 12 and 13 by anything better than the mean lines parallel to the δ-axis. It is not difficult to prove that the mean line of fig. 12 would make the acceleration factor equal to $+5 \cdot 3$ whereas the mean line of fig. 13 would make it $+1$. Hence such an attitude of extreme pessimism regarding Sandage's work fails to shake the conclusion that the acceleration is negative. Indeed it may be thought to reinforce the suggestion that a value for the acceleration factor equal to about 3 is a possible one.

Turning now to the second objection, it may be that there are clusters whose membership is small and whose brightest members may consequently be intrinsically less luminous than are those of well populated clusters. Abell has given a criterion for the 'richness' of a cluster and it does turn out that clusters 1, 6, 10 and 12 are poorer than the rest that have been employed in figs. 12 and 13. But, as far as the present author can determine, the degree of richness of the remainder shows no systematic tendency to increase with the red-shift. Hence the distribution of the points in figs. 12 and 13 is unlikely to be systematically affected by lack of comparability amongst clusters.

The last objection is a very interesting one and is due to Elizabeth Scott [38]. Granted that evolutionary changes may be insufficient to produce a value of W_1 sensibly different from zero, it is possible to imagine that selection could assign a non-zero value to this quantity. When clusters are being chosen for measurements of red-shift, it is conceivable that the observer, as he seeks larger and larger red-shifts, will unconsciously choose clusters that contain giant galaxies of progressively greater and greater intrinsic luminosities. If this is so, then the absolute magnitude of the synthetic brightest member galaxy will have had the U-property spuriously imposed on it. It would not then be justifiable to assume that W_1 was zero in deducing the value of the acceleration factor from the slope of the lines (a) or (b) in figs. 12 or 13. Therefore, the value of the factor would remain essentially unknown, since there is no way of estimating the amount of the spurious W_1. That an effect of this kind is imaginable is one thing; that any sound observational evidence for its existence is available is quite another. We do not even know that observational evidence for such an effect would ever be obtainable. But should it be, we must await the production of the evidence and the value of W_1 to which it would give rise. Meanwhile we may apply the principle mentioned in Chapter 1, namely, that the existence of an imaginable datum of unknown value should not prevent the drawing of conclusions from those data which we do possess.

Summarizing the discussion of the observations on the redshifts of clusters of galaxies, it may be said that the Hubble parameter H lies somewhere in the range of 100 to 160 km/sec/mpc. That H cannot be pinned down more accurately is principally due to the uncertainty in the absolute magnitude that is to be assigned to the synthetic brightest galaxy in a cluster. As to the acceleration factor q_0, the most pessimistic deduction from the data is that it lies between 1 and 5; but there is also good reason for believing that q_0 lies in the range* 1 to 3. Hence the model universe which best appears to fit the data is one in which the rate of expansion is being slowed down at the present time. This in turn means that the

---

* Humason, Mayall and Sandage [21], by more elaborate methods than we have used, deduce that $q_0 = 3 \pm 0.8$ for the photographic magnitudes that were also employed in Figs. 12 and 13. Photovisual magnitudes yield a smaller value and Hoyle and Sandage [39] have suggested $q_0 = 2.5 \pm 1$ as an over-all average.

scale-factor for the model must be a function of t such that its second derivative with respect to the time has a negative value at the present moment. Scale-factors which do not possess this property are excluded from the range of possibilities, if our analysis of the red-shift data is accepted.

The Hubble Parameter and the Virgo Cluster

In the preceding sections the Hubble parameter and the acceleration parameter have been determined from the red-shift data on clusters of galaxies. There is a distance-scale involved in these investigations though it enters in a disguised form. This scale is represented by the absolute magnitude assigned to the synthetic brightest member of a cluster, because, as was seen in Chapter 2, this absolute magnitude was selected by estimating the distances of galaxies relatively close to our own. It therefore suggests itself that a direct determination of the Hubble parameter could be obtained by finding the distance corresponding to some particular value of the red-shift. The first approximation to formula (16) of Chapter 5 may be written as $h_1 = c\delta/D$. Therefore if the luminosity-distance D and the red-shift of some object could be found independently of each other, the value of the Hubble parameter could be calculated.

The Virgo cluster of galaxies with a red-shift of 0·004 is probably the nearest object to which the method could be applied. It is true that the rather peculiar position occupied by the cluster point for the Virgo cluster on figs. 12 and 13 might make us hesitate in using this cluster alone to determine the Hubble parameter. However a careful and detailed study of the cluster has been made by Holmberg, who concludes that its distance-modulus is 30·2 and that our own Galaxy is responsible for an obscuration of 0·26 mags. in the direction of the cluster. Thus the true distance-modulus is 29·94. Taking account of the errors involved, Holmberg [13] arrives at a value of H equal to 134 ± 6 km/sec/mpc. Nevertheless an examination of his work suggests that it would be safer to say that H lies in the range 128 to 147 km/sec/mpc. This falls within the limits of 100 to 160 km/sec/mpc which we have derived from the data represented by figs. 12 and 13.

In contrast to the foregoing results, Sandage [7] has argued that H may lie in the range 50 to 100 km/sec/mpc. He adopts the nova method of distance determination as preferable to all others but supplements it by a distance criterion based on the apparent magnitudes of the brightest stars in certain galaxies resolved by Hubble in 1936. These include galaxies in the Virgo cluster. The reliability of the conclusions depends on the degree of faith we attach to the accuracy of the calibration of the nova method and of the brightest star method. We have already noticed how precarious is the calibration of the first method with respect to novae in our Galaxy. As to the brightest stars, the absolute magnitudes of only three in our Galaxy are quoted and they lie in the range $-8 \cdot 8$ to $-9 \cdot 8$. A few more absolute magnitudes of stars in the two Magellanic Clouds and in the galaxies M 31, M 33 and NGC 6822 are listed by Sandage. But since the absolute magnitudes are obtainable only when the distances of the galaxies are known, they hardly provide strong support for the calibration. Thus Sandage's low values of H must for the present be treated with reserve, as he himself suggests.

This discussion of the direct determination of the Hubble parameter serves to emphasize one important point, namely, that this parameter varies inversely with the luminosity-distances computed for nearby galaxies. The value of the parameter is therefore a convenient way of expressing the scale of distance that is being employed for all those galaxies whose red-shifts are small and which are consequently near to our own.

Luminosity-distance and Red-shift

The partial knowledge of the nature of the model universe provided by the values of the Hubble and acceleration parameters makes possible the calculation of the luminosity-distance of an object whose red-shift is known. The truncated form of equation (16), Chapter 5, is employed for the purpose, namely,

$$D = \frac{c\delta}{H} \left\{ 1 + \tfrac{1}{2} (1 - q_0) \, \delta \right\} .$$

Here c is measured in km/sec and H in km/sec/mpc so that D is obtained at once in megaparsecs. When the red-shift is small, the term in curly brackets is unity to a sufficient degree of accuracy. The luminosity-distance then, of course, depends only on the selected value of H. But when the red-shift is appreciable, the acceleration factor influences the luminosity-distance to an important extent as may be seen by considering the case of the Hydra cluster of galaxies. The red-shift of the cluster is 0·2, to a sufficient accuracy. If we take H in the range 100 to 160 km/sec/mpc and q_0 equal to 3, the luminosity-distance of the cluster lies in the range of 300 to 480 mpc. But suppose that it was decided to employ instead the values of the parameters deduced from line (*b*) of fig. 12, namely, H in the range 134 to 212 km/sec/mpc and $q_0 = -7\cdot2$. The luminosity-distance now turns out to lie in the interval 515 to 815 mpc. The change of model for the universe has therefore increased the computed distance of the Hydra cluster by something like 65 per cent. In Chapter 3 the local distance of the cluster was found to be 540 to 860 megaparsec, a result that really depended on the use of the model universe of classical physics in which all objects were at relative rest and no account was taken of the red-shift. It happens that this local distance is roughly equal to that found for the model universe corresponding to line (*b*) of fig. 12. This leads to the suspicion that a system of galaxies could move in such a fashion that their luminosity-distances would mimic local distances, a conclusion already arrived at, for a somewhat different reason, with regard to Class II radio sources. But in any case, the important point is that the distances – unlike the red-shifts – of remote objects are much influenced by the choice of model universe and no unique values can be assigned to them on the basis of presently available knowledge.

The same is true of the travel-time of the radiation and therefore of the moment in the past at which a galaxy with appreciable red-shift is being seen. The predicted travel-time* from the Hydra cluster, on the basis of line (a) of fig. 13, is 0.64×10^9 to 1.0×10^9 years. But, from fig. 12, line (b), on the other hand, we have 1.4×10^9 to 2.2×10^9 years. Both models do agree in one respect: the travel-times are enormously large on the human scale and they therefore justify the statement that the whole history of astronomy can be regarded in cosmology as compressed into a single 'instant' of time.

The Curvature of Space and the Cosmical Constant

A determination of the Hubble parameter and the acceleration factor also makes it possible to go a little further with the selection of the model universe that best represents the observed universe. We can now seek to find the space-curvature constant k and this will entail a simultaneous determination of the cosmical constant. The new element of theory is provided by the Einstein field equations (equation (4), Chapter 4). When they are worked out for the general model universe whose metric is given in equation (1) of Chapter 5, it turns out that there are two Einstein equations, namely,

*An approximate formula, derived from equation (8) of Chapter 5, is
$$t_0 - t = \frac{\delta}{h_1} \left\{ 1 - (1 + \tfrac{1}{2} q_0) \delta \right\} .$$

$$8\pi G\rho = 3\left(\frac{R'}{R}\right)^2 + \frac{3kc^2}{R^2} - \lambda , \tag{5}$$

$$8\pi G\frac{p}{c^2} = -2\frac{R''}{R} - \left(\frac{R'}{R}\right)^2 - \frac{kc^2}{R^2} + \lambda . \tag{6}$$

The first equation gives the density, ρ, of the representative gas and the second, the pressure p. As before, a prime denotes a derivative of the scale-factor with respect to the time and it will be assumed that ordinary c.g.s. units are employed, the time being in seconds and the scale-factor in cm. These equations are valid at all times and therefore in particular at the present moment, t_0. Let therefore the present values of the density and pressure be denoted by ρ_0 and p_0 respectively. The Hubble and acceleration parameters, h_1 and h_2, are, of course, equal to the present values of R'/R and R''/R, respectively. A ratio which is important for our purpose is that of $4\pi G\rho_0$ to h_1^2 and it will be denoted by σ_0. The two Einstein equations can then be evaluated at the instant t_0 and re-arranged so as to express the cosmical constant λ and the combination kc^2/R_0^2 in terms of the other quantities. In fact

$$\lambda = (\sigma_0 - 3q_0)h_1^2 + 12\pi G\frac{p_0}{c^2} , \tag{7}$$

$$\frac{kc^2}{R_0^2} = (\sigma_0 - q_0 - 1)h_1^2 + 4\pi G\frac{p_0}{c^2} . \tag{8}$$

Hence if it proves possible to compute the right hand sides of these equations from observational data the cosmical constant λ, the space-curvature constant k and the magnitude of the scale-factor at the present moment, R_0, would all be determined.

We begin with the computation of σ_0, a number which depends on the present density of matter in the model universe. This can be identified with the average density of matter in the observed universe in the cosmical neighbourhood of our Galaxy. An estimate of this density was made by Oort [40] in 1958 using a distance scale in which H was 75 km/sec/mpc ($h_1 = 2\cdot43 \times 10^{-18}\text{sec}^{-1}$). There are, of course, uncertainties in making an estimate of this kind arising from such factors as the adopted ratio of the mass to the luminosity of a galaxy, the number of galaxies per unit volume and their distances. However, in Oort's opinion, the average density of matter at present is $3\cdot1 \times 10^{-31}$ gr/cm³, though it is possible that this quantity might have to be multiplied by a factor 'of ten or more'. Now H and h_1 are inversely proportional to the distances used. Suppose, therefore, that it is decided that the value of H should be altered to $75f$ km/sec/mpc, where f is some numerical factor. This would mean that all distances were reduced by the factor $1/f$ as compared with those employed by Oort, and this has two consequences. Firstly, his density must be multiplied by f^3 because of the reduction in the size of each unit volume. But, secondly, the density must also be multiplied by $1/f$ because of the methods by which the masses of galaxies are found. They entail the consequence that the mass of a galaxy is proportional to the scale of distance. The net result is that, when $H = 75f$ km/sec/mpc the density is $3\cdot1f^2 \times 10^{-31}$ gr/cm³. Also H and h_1 are proportional to one another and $G = 6\cdot668 \times 10^{-8}$ cm/gr/sec². Hence σ_0 is independent of f and its value is

$$\sigma_0 = \frac{4\pi G\rho_0}{h_1{}^2} = \frac{4\pi(6\cdot668 \times 10^{-8}) \times (3\cdot1 \times 10^{-31})f^2}{(2\cdot43 \times 10^{-18})^2 f^2} = 0\cdot044.$$

Multiplication of Oort's density by a factor of ten would, of course, raise the value of σ_0 to $0\cdot44$.

In the course of the discussion of special world-lines in Chapter 5, it was suggested that the pressure of the representative gas gave a measure of the non-material energy in the universe. Thus p_0 would be the measure of this energy at the present time. The important question is the magnitude of the quantity p_0/c^2, which is expressible in the same units as density, compared with ρ_0. It is usually stated that p_0/c^2 cannot at present exceed $10^{-5} \rho_0$, but an up-to-date observational derivation of this result is lacking. The conclusion appears to be based on the work of de Sitter [41] carried out in 1930. He assumed that the pressure was mainly due to radiation and to the kinetic energy of galaxies arising from their random motions, over and above the general velocity of expansion. For what it is worth, a plausibility argument for the smallness of the pressure as compared with the density can be constructed as follows: Suppose that all the non-material energy of the observed universe is allocated to the representative gas as the kinetic energy of agitation of its particles. Suppose also that the particles are hydrogen atoms. Then the representative gas would form a so-called perfect gas in which the ratio of p_0 to ρ_0 would be proportional to the temperature of the gas. It can then be calculated that if $p_0/c^2 = 10^{-5} \rho_0$, the temperature of the representative gas would have to be of the order of 100 million degrees. Such temperatures occur in the observed universe only in the centres of hot stars. It is difficult to see how there could be enough non-material energy available in the observed universe to produce a representative gas of so high a temperature. Hence it may be concluded that *at the present time*, p_0/c^2 is negligibly small compared with ρ_0. Therefore the terms in equations (7) and (8) involving Gp_0/c^2 can be neglected compared with the rest, which are of the order of magnitude of $G\rho_0$, and the two equations reduce to

$$\lambda = -(3q_0 - \sigma_0)h_1^2, \tag{9}$$

$$\frac{kc^2}{R_0^2} = -(q_0 + 1 - \sigma_0)h_1^2. \tag{10}$$

It has already been suggested that q_0 lies in the range 1 to 3 and that σ_0 is 0·044. Therefore the factors $-(3q_0 - \sigma_0)$ and

$-(q_0 + 1 - \sigma_0)$ are negative numbers, a conclusion that persists even if the value of σ_0 is raised to 0·44. It therefore follows that the cosmical constant is negative and that the space-curvature constant is equal to -1. The second conclusion means that space is hyperbolic and that its volume at any instant of time is therefore infinite in extent. Such a universe also contains an infinite amount of matter.

A non-zero value of the cosmical constant is distasteful to some cosmologists who wish, mainly on aesthetic grounds, to omit it from general relativity theory. If then λ is set equal to zero, it must follow that $3q_0 = \sigma_0$ and therefore that σ_0 should lie between 3 and 9. This in turn would imply that the present density of matter in the universe would have to be multiplied by a factor of between 70 and 200 which is a long way off the factor 'of ten or more' by which Oort believes his average density might be modified. Predicted densities larger than the observed have indeed always dogged the footsteps of those who, without inquiry, make the cosmical constant zero. Another consequence of this assumption can be seen from equation (10). If λ is zero, then $\sigma_0 = 3q_0$ and it necessarily follows that $\sigma_0 - q_0 - 1$ is positive, because q_0 is at least unity. Thus $k = +1$ which makes space spherical and so of finite volume. The value assigned to the cosmical constant therefore has far reaching consequences; its magnitude cannot be left to individual predilection but must be found from observation.

A negative value of λ means, as was mentioned in Chapter 4, that there exists a universal force in the universe which tends to prevent the galaxies from flying apart. This force is additional to the mutual gravitational attractions between galaxies. These two forces between them account for the retardation of the expansion indicated by the negative acceleration parameter. But if the λ-force is abolished by the assertion that the cosmical constant is zero, all the responsi-

K

bility for the retardation is thrown on to gravitation. The observed universe does not apparently contain enough matter to produce the retardation. Therefore the amount of matter has to be increased from 70 to 200 times in order to compensate for the abolition of the λ-force. Our prejudices may be offended by the presence of this force, particularly if we are convinced that we know already all the forces that can possibly act in the observed universe. But a view which is perhaps more scientific is to follow where the facts and the theory lead even if as a result, a new problem presents itself. This concerns the nature of the λ-force and its relation to such other large-scale forces as gravitation or the magnetic fields that occur within galaxies. There is at the moment no answer to this question: it forms one of the problems that has been produced by the study of cosmology.

Particular Model Universes in General Relativity

The observational data therefore give the values of the Hubble parameter, of the acceleration parameter and, with a lesser degree of certainty, of the space-curvature and the cosmical constant. The two parameters do not by themselves define the scale-factor function $R(t)$ for all values of t and therefore observation fails to select a particular model universe. There is however a theoretical method for choosing particular model universes in general relativity which is based on Einstein's equations (5) and (6) above. These two equations are however mathematically indeterminate in the sense that there are two equations for three unknowns. They are the density, the pressure and the scale-factor. Therefore each particular model universe derived from Einstein's equations contains an arbitrary element, amounting to a statement regarding the dependence on the time of one of the three unknown functions. In the construction of particular models it is customary to go further than this and to assign specific values to one or other of the two constants, k and λ, that occur in Einstein's equations. The cosmical constant is usually the victim in this operation. These points may be illustrated by the consideration of a few particular model universes.

We begin with Milne's model whose specifications are $R=ct$ and $k=-1$. The Hubble parameter h_1 is therefore $1/t_0$ and the acceleration parameter h_2 is zero. The model shows how inapplicable a name for h_1 (or H) is the term 'Hubble constant'. Clearly h_1 varies with the time since it is inversely proportional to the instant at which the observations are made. The vanishing of the acceleration parameter suggests that the representative gas is moving under the action of no forces. This suggestion finds confirmation in Einstein's equations which reduce to

$$8\pi G\rho = -8\pi Gp/c^2 = \lambda.$$

Therefore the density and pressure must have opposite signs; if the one is positive, the other must be negative. A negative density for the representative gas hardly seems to be plausible on physical grounds; a negative pressure is perhaps less objectionable but is a far-fetched possibility. The conclusion usually drawn is that Milne's model – in its general relativity interpretation – refers to a highly idealized state in which both gravitational effects and the influence of the λ-force are vanishingly small. Mathematically this means that the foregoing equations are satisfied by putting ρ, p, and λ all separately equal to zero. In spite of its artificiality Milne's model is useful because it describes a motion of expansion under no forces.

A similar kind of interest attaches to one of the earliest particular models to be discovered. It is the de Sitter universe in which R is an exponential function of the time and the curvature of space is zero so that we may write

$$R=R_0 e^{(t-t_0)/T}, \quad k=0, \tag{11}$$

where R_0 is the value of R at the present moment, t_0, and T is a constant. Einstein's equations then again give

$$8\pi G\rho = -8\pi Gp/c^2 = \frac{3}{T^2} - \lambda.$$

As in Milne's model, we reject negative pressures and densities, and we are left with only one possibility. This is that $8\pi G\rho$ and $8\pi Gp/c^2$ are both zero which can be interpreted by saying that gravitational effects are negligible. The cosmical constant must be positive and $T=(3/\lambda)^{1/2}$. Moreover it also follows from the definition of R in the de Sitter universe that

$$h_1 = \frac{1}{T} = \left(\frac{\lambda}{3}\right)^{1/2},$$

$$h_2 = \frac{1}{T^2} = \frac{\lambda}{3} = h_1{}^2.$$

The motion of the infinitely rare representative gas in this model therefore proceeds at an ever increasing rate, since h_2 is positive. The Hubble parameter has become a 'constant of nature' because it is proportional to the square root of the cosmical constant. It may be argued that the de Sitter universe shows what would happen if the λ-force were a repulsion ($\lambda>0$) and gravitation were absent. But it can only do this at the price of introducing a representative gas of zero density as might be anticipated because any appreciable amount of matter would certainly have some gravitational effect.

The earliest in order of discovery of the particular model universes was the Einstein universe in which the repulsion represented by a positive cosmical constant just balances the gravitational attraction between the different parts of the representative gas. If R is taken to be a constant, say, R_e, in Einstein's equations then negative densities and pressures are avoided if k is chosen to be $+1$ and λ is positive. Then also

$$8\pi G \rho_e = \frac{3c^2}{R_e{}^2} - \lambda,$$

$$8\pi G \frac{p_e}{c^2} = \lambda - \frac{c^2}{R_e{}^2},$$

and therefore if we follow Einstein and assert that $p_e = 0$, it follows that

$$4\pi G \rho_e = \frac{c^2}{R_e{}^2} = \lambda.$$

Since R now does not depend on t, the representative gas is not in motion and h_1 and h_2 are both zero. Space is spherical because $k = +1$ and its total volume can be shown to be $2\pi^2 R_e{}^3$. Multiplying this by the density ρ_e gives the total mass of representative gas in the model, namely

$$m_e = 2\pi^2 R_e{}^3 \rho_e = \frac{1}{2}\frac{\pi}{G}c^2 R_e = \frac{1}{2}\frac{\pi}{G}\frac{c^3}{\lambda^{1/2}}.$$

It is sometimes argued as if these relations between ρ_e, R_e, λ and m_e were laws of nature predicted by general relativity and valid in all uniform model universes. This is certainly not the case; they hold good in the Einstein universe only, a model which is incapable of accounting for the red-shift phenomenon. It is therefore quite illegitimate, for example, to identify ρ_e with the average density in the observed universe at the present time and to deduce that this observed density is proportional to the cosmical constant.

These three particular models are characterized by having acceleration parameters which are either zero or positive. If observation suggests that this parameter should be negative, it is necessary to look further afield amongst particular models. In searching for them via Einstein's equations the usual procedure has been to guess at the value of one of the two constants k and λ and to put the pressure equal to zero. Whereas one can argue with some plausibility that the non-material energy in the observed universe is at present negligibly small compared with the density, it is a very much longer shot to assert that this has always been so. Yet it is precisely this which is assumed in the so-called zero pressure particular models. When the galaxies were all far closer together than they are now, it is by no means self-evident that the non-material energy in the observed universe would still be small compared with the density. A zero pressure model is therefore one which can describe the observed universe for a length of time into the past during which conditions do not differ radically from those at present observed. Such models could not be expected to account for the early stages of the expansion when congestion would be likely to destroy the very basic condition by which all models are set up, namely that of uniformity.

The simplest of the zero pressure particular models is the Einstein-de Sitter universe which has the specifications

$$R = R_0 \left(\frac{t}{t_0} \right)^{2/3}, \ k = 0, \ \lambda = 0,$$

where R_0 is the value of R at the present moment, t_0. It is easy to show from Einstein's equations that the pressure is zero throughout the history of this model, except at the initial instance $t = 0$ when it is undefined. The density of the representative gas at any time t is given by

$$4\pi G\rho = \frac{2}{3} \frac{1}{t^2}$$

and is thus infinitely large at the initial instant $t = 0$ and tends to zero as the time increases to infinity. The Hubble and acceleration parameters are, respectively,

$$h_1 = \frac{2}{3} \frac{1}{t_0},$$

$$h_2 = -\frac{2}{9} \frac{1}{t_0^2} = -\tfrac{1}{2} h_1^2,$$

and the predicted present density is therefore given by

$$4\pi G\rho_0 = \frac{3}{2}h_1{}^2.$$

This model has many attractive features: the scale-factor R is a relatively simple function of the time, space is Euclidean, the acceleration parameter is negative and there is no cosmical constant to worry about. But it has disadvantages from the observational point of view: the acceleration factor is necessarily 1/2, which is too small, and σ_0 is predicted to be exactly 1·5, which is 34 times too large. The second conclusion would mean that astronomers have only been able to identify some 3 per cent of the material present in the universe, even in those parts of it that are easily accessible to observation. The model, in fact, illustrates how a zero cosmical constant produces too large a density of matter, even when the retardation is small. Like most particular models, the Einstein-de Sitter predicts too much and too accurately what 'ought' to be observed.

A feature of the Einstein-de Sitter universe that is worth noticing is that R is zero at $t=0$. This implies that all the representative gas would be compressed into an infinitely small volume at this moment. It is usual in cosmology to take literally a prediction of this kind and to identify the instant $t=0$ with the moment of 'creation', or as that of the 'beginning of time'. The 'age of the universe' is then said to be the lapse of time from this instant to the present moment. Now in the Einstein-de Sitter universe $t_0 = \frac{2}{3}(1/h_1)$ and therefore the age of the universe is calculable from the Hubble parameter. If, indeed, $H=100$ km/sec/mpc, the age comes out as $6·5 \times 10^9$ years and if $H=160$ km/sec/mpc, then at $4·1 \times 10^9$ years. In the present author's opinion, this procedure over-interprets the theory in so far as its application to the observed universe is concerned. Going backwards in time, we can legitimately expect that, long before $R=0$ is reached, conditions similar to those that prevail at present in the observed universe would have broken down. Thus the uniform model universes would cease to apply. An age of the universe calculated from a particular model universe in the manner indicated above – and all ages deduced from the expansion are of this kind – gives merely an upper limit to the period during which the presently prevailing conditions in the observed universe might be expected to have lasted. What happened before that, and for how long, must await the development of a theory of non-uniform models or, at least, of models in which the pressure is not always zero. Studies are now under way in Germany [42] and in Russia [43] and one interesting fact has already emerged: the existence of an initial instant at which $R=0$ is a consequence of the extreme simplicity of constitution attributed to the representative gas. If the expansion is not quite the same in different directions or if a local spinning motion, in addition to the expansion, occurs, then the vanishing of the scale-factor is either modified in character or is avoided altogether. Thus the 'big bang' that is supposed to correspond to the initial instant, or 'moment of creation', is a product of the idealization process by which an oversimplified representative gas replaces the material content of the observed universe.

The zero pressure particular model universes have been classified in detail, a classification that depends on the selected combination of $+1$, 0 or -1 for the space-curvature constant k together with a zero, positive or negative cosmical constant. The interested reader can consult the literature on this point [44]. If the point of view is accepted that the presently available data suggest negative values for λ and k, then those zero pressure models that satisfy these conditions are of special interest. In this group R is a complicated function of t which begins by being zero at $t=0$, increases to a maximum and then decreases to zero again. The models are therefore of the repetitive or oscillating type. Within the group they differ in detail from one another according to the selected combinations of σ_0 and q_0. Fig. 16 illustrates the

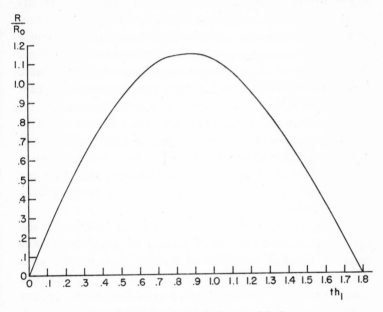

FIG. 16. Change of scale-factor with time.

march of R against time for a model in which $\sigma_0 = 0.06$ and $q_0 = 3.06$. In the figure, R is plotted relative to the present value R_0 as unit and the time, with $1/h_1$ as unit. The time-lapse from $R=0$ to the present moment is 0.58 $(1/h_1)$ which compares with the 0.67 $(1/h_1)$ of the Einstein-de Sitter model. Thus there is a reduction of a little over 13 per cent in the time-lapse. A complete cycle from $R=0$ and back again occupies a time of 1.8 $(1/h_1)$ or roughly three times the time-lapse from $R=0$ to the present moment.

Particular model universes lead to the resolution of Olbers' paradox. Olbers pointed out that, if sources of radiation are distributed uniformly, and at mutual rest, in the universe of classical physics, then the night sky ought to be brilliantly illuminated whereas it is observed to be dark. This contradiction indeed constitutes one of the most powerful reasons for discarding the classical model. The red-shift does away with Olbers' conclusion because the diminution of illumination that the red-shift entails means that the total background radiation in a model universe is very small [45]. For example, if the model is Milne's and the total flux-density of all radio sources within the model is computed, the amount of radiation received would be equal to that from a portion only of a classical universe. This portion consists of a sphere, centred at the observer, of radius $c/\{h_1 (1-x)\}$, where x is the spectral index of the radio sources. Correspondingly small amounts are obtained when the optical radiation at all frequencies is calculated [46].

In conclusion it is worth examining the statement that the particular model universes of general relativity are 'evolutionary', a description often applied to them. Evolution is legitimately attributed to individual objects in the observed universe. Thus a star may be said to evolve because, in the course of time, its chemical composition alters, or it loses or acquires mass, or its luminosity changes. An interstellar gas cloud may go through a sequence of states that ultimately transform it into a star; and so on. Such developments are comparable to those that have occurred in the forms of animal life on this earth during the lapse of geological time. But they are connected with the discreteness of astronomical objects in the observed universe, a discreteness which is abolished for the representative gas that fills a model universe. With this idealization, the concept of evolution goes by the board also. In fact, what is meant by an 'evolutionary' model universe is simply one in which the density and pressure of the representative gas vary with the time. That this situation carries with it no implication of evolution is easily seen. Suppose that the observed universe contained only billiard balls, each one of which was absolutely immutable in time with respect to all its physical properties. No billiard ball would therefore evolve in the sense that a star does. Suppose also that the billiard balls were in a state of mutual recession from one another. Then the representative gas that would replace them in a model universe could have a density and pressure that varied with time. But this variation, which reflects the motion of recession combined with the immutability of mass for each billiard ball, tells us nothing about the (non-existent) evolution of each object. In other words, the treatment of an evolving universe in general relativity must await the solution of the formidable mathematical problems that arise when the discreteness of astronomical objects has to be taken into account.

Model Universes and Class II Radio sources

This section will be devoted to the consideration of some problems connected with the observed properties of Class II radio sources. In particular, it will be interesting to consider the red-shifts and distances that correspond to the limits of flux-density in such a survey as the Australian, and also to investigate how the distribution law given by equation (5) of Chapter 3 comes about.

It has been mentioned that very few Class II radio sources have been identified with optical objects whose distances are known. Therefore the approximate method employed in discussing the optical red-shift data is no longer legitimate. This method assumed that the red-shifts were of modest size compared with unity. But, for aught we know, the Class II radio sources might be so remote that their red-shifts would be equal to, or exceed, unity. Therefore exact relations between luminosity-distance and red-shift must now be brought into play. Such relations are only accessible when R is known as a specific function of t and this is merely another way of saying that a particular model universe must be available. Since the optical data do not permit of the selection of one particular model universe, all that can be done is to pick one or more models as specimens and investigate what happens in them. Three models will be chosen for the discussion of the red-shift and distance problem on the ground that the models are mathematically as simple as possible. They are Milne's model, the Einstein-de Sitter and the de Sitter universe, whose specifications have already been given.

In a particular model universe, exact equations between luminosity-distance and red-shift, and between flux-density and red-shift, can be worked out. It is advisable to avoid absolute values and to express luminosity-distances and flux-densities in the form of ratios of these quantities relative to those of a standard source [47]. The crude assumption is also made that all Class II sources have the same intrinsic power output as the selected standard source. The choice of the latter is limited because it must be one which has been identified with an optical source in order that its luminosity-distance can be estimated and its red-shift measured. The safest procedure at the present time is to choose two extreme possibilities, one comparatively weak and nearby source, and one very powerful and remote one. For the weak source, the galaxy NGC 1275 is chosen. It is a member of the Perseus cluster of galaxies whose red-shift is $\delta_s=0\cdot018$. A rough estimate of its luminosity-distance D_s is therefore 54 to 34 megaparsec according as H is equal to 100 km/sec/mpc or to 160 km/sec/mpc. The flux-density of this source as measured by Mills's radio telescope is $S_s=240\times10^{-26}$ w m^{-2} (c/s)$^{-1}$. The powerful and remote source will be chosen to be Cygnus A, whose red-shift is $\delta_s=0\cdot056$. Thus its luminosity-distance D_s lies roughly in the range 168 to 105 megaparsec for the same values of H. The flux-density is $S_s = 19,000 \times 10^{-26}$ w m^{-2} (c/s)$^{-1}$. The results of the computations of the red-shifts corresponding to the successive limits of flux-density in the Australian survey are shown in columns two to seven of Table I. The spectral index has been given the value $x = -0.75$. The interesting features of this Table are: if NGC 1275 is typical of Class II radio sources, the effect of using different model universes is small. From the red-shifts, it can be concluded that the sources in the survey lie at distances that fall between that of the Coma cluster of galaxies ($\delta = 0.022$) and a distance somewhat less than that of the Boötes cluster ($\delta = 0.131$). If this is so, the difficulty in optical identification of the Class II sources must be due mainly to the ambiguities in their radio positions, because galaxies in this range of red-shift are easily recorded on the Sky Atlas.

TABLE I

Red-shift and Flux-density ($x = -0.75$)

$S \times 10^{26}$	NGC 1275 as standard			Cygnus A as standard		
	Milne	Einstein– de Sitter	de Sitter*	Milne	Einstein– de Sitter	de Sitter*
7	·102	·105	·100	1·79	2·64	1·42
10	·086	·087	·084	1·573	2·22	1·257
20	·062	·062	·060	1·210	1·56	·990
40	·044	·044	·043	·925	1·14	·771
80	·031	·031	·031	·699	·815	·600
160	·022	·022	·022	·521	·584	·460

* Also valid for the steady-state theory.

But the situation is quite different if Cygnus A is typical of Class II radio sources. A glance down the last three columns of Table I shows that a change of model now makes a considerable alteration in the red-shift for a given flux-density. Moreover the red-shifts are enormous; so much so, that even the upper limit of flux-density, 160×10^{-26} w m^{-2} (c/s)$^{-1}$, now corresponds to a luminosity-distance so large that galaxies of this remoteness are barely recorded on the Sky Atlas. The reader is reminded that red-shifts greater than unity occur because relativistic Doppler formulae are in use. The lack of optical identifications now becomes intelligible: the majority of sources are so remote that it is unlikely that their images could be recorded by the photographic plate.

The large red-shifts entailed by the choice of Cygnus A as standard source have another consequence. One of the curious properties of certain particular models of the universe is that they impose a finite limit to the distance of an object. Sometimes both the luminosity-distance and the distance by apparent size can possess this property; in other models the distance by apparent size is alone limited [48]. To the second category belongs the Einstein-de Sitter universe; in Milne's model and the de Sitter universe both kinds of distance are unlimited in magnitude. The apparent angular diameter of an extended source of radiation of small intrinsic size is inversely proportional to its distance by apparent size, ξ. Therefore if all Class II radio sources have equal and small cross-sections, there must be, in the Einstein-de Sitter universe, a lower limit of angular diameter corresponding to the maximum value of ξ. It can be proved that the minimum angular diameter will occur at a red-shift of $1 \cdot 25$. The sixth column of Table I indicates that this corresponds to a critical flux-density lying between 40×10^{-26} and 20×10^{-26} w m^{-2} (c/s)$^{-1}$, provided, of course, that the sources were all as powerful as Cygnus A. The angular diameters would decrease up to the stage when the critical flux-density was reached, but thereafter they would begin to increase again. Clearly, however, the presence of this effect depends on the strength of the selected standard source. If NGC 1275 represented this source, nothing would be observed simply because all the Class II radio sources would be too close to our Galaxy. It is, in fact, highly probable that the most frequently occurring Class II radio source would have an intrinsic power output intermediate between that of NGC 1275 and of Cygnus A. Hence, if observation revealed no minimum angular diameter, two interpretations would be possible. One would be that the model universe predicted the effect, but the critical flux-density had not been reached by the observers. The other would be that the model belonged to the category in which there was no minimum of angular diameter.

The ratio of the luminosity-distance at each value of S to the luminosity-distance of the standard source can also be computed. These ratios are exhibited in Table II, again for

TABLE II

Limiting Flux-densities and Distance-ratios

$S \times 10^{26}$	NGC 1275 as standard	Cygnus A as Standard			
		l/l	D/D_s		
	$l/l_s \sim D/D_s$		Milne	Einstein–de Sitter	de Sitter*
7	5·86	52·1	58·8	60·8	57·8
10	4·90	43·6	48·4	50·1	47·9
20	3·46	30·8	33·8	34·4	33·4
40	2·45	21·8	23·5	23·8	23·3
80	1·73	15·4	16·3	16·5	16·2
160	1·22	10·9	11·4	11·5	11·4

* Also valid for the steady-state theory.

$x = -0.75$. When NGC 1275 is the standard source all three models give essentially the same results. The distance-ratios are also approximately equal to the ratios of local distances computed from (3) of Chapter 2. When Cygnus A is chosen as standard source, the three models yield luminosity-distance ratios that differ little from one another, in contrast to what happened for the red-shifts. The local distance ratios are systematically smaller than the luminosity-distance ratios, because of the presence of the red-shift factor in formula (17) of Chapter 5. Since $x = -0.75$, this factor is

$$\left(\frac{1+\delta}{1+\delta_s}\right)^{1/8}$$

and its value is never large for the red-shifts of Table I.

Turning next to the problem of distribution in depth, the questions to be answered are: can the theory of model universes throw any light on the empirical relationship (5) of Chapter 3 in which the total number of sources counted varies as the $-\frac{1}{2}(3+\mu)$ power of the limiting flux-density? Can the motion of the sources, consequent on identifying them with galaxies, be the origin of the non-zero values of μ suggested by the Australian and Cambridge surveys, or would a zero value of μ be equally unexpected? Answers to these questions can be found by considering the theory of the number-density of sources in a model universe [49].

Since a Class II radio source is identified with a galaxy, its world-line will be a special one or, in other words, its r-co-ordinate in the space-time of a model universe is fixed. Thus once a source is located in Shell r of fig. 11 it will always remain in that shell. Suppose that $t = t_1$ is the instant when the scale-factor R has the value unity. This instant can be imagined as being a moment in the remote past. The volume* of Shell r is dv at that moment, and we may say that the number-density of sources in the shell is then $\alpha(t_1)dv$

---

* The theory of the space-time (1), Chapter 5, shows that

$$dv = \frac{4\pi r^2 dr}{(1+kr^2/4)^3},$$

if the thickness of the shell is dr.

sources. At a later time $t=t_2$ the scale-factor $R(t_2)$ has increased to a value greater than unity and the volume of the shell is now $R^3(t_2)dv$. Thus the number-density will have fallen to a fraction $1/R^3(t_2)$ of its former value due to the expansion. But it is conceivable that a radio source is sufficiently strong to be observed, only for a short period in its lifetime. For example, a collision between two galaxies can apparently produce a radio source. Such a collision may be an evanescent phenomenon on the cosmic scale of time and, in any case, new collisions may occur during the interval t_1 to t_2. These possibilities can be allowed for by assigning the U-property to a and thus permitting it to vary with the time. Hence the number-density in Shell r would be $a(t_2)/R^3(t_2)$ at the instant t_2.

The number of sources in Shell r will appear to the human observer to be determined by the state of affairs at the departure-time, t, of the radiation. At that moment the number-density of sources in the shell will be $n=a(t)/R^3(t)$. But the departure-time can be replaced by the red-shift appropriate to the Shell and it is also true that $R(t)$ is equal to $R_0/(1+\delta)$, where R_0 is the scale-factor computed at the arrival-time t_0. Hence, from the observer's point of view, the number-density of sources in Shell r is

$$n = \frac{a(\delta)(1+\delta)^3}{R_0^3}.$$

It is here advantageous to introduce a 'standard' number-density with which to compare the number-density in any Shell. The standard number-density may be taken to be n_s, which is that in the nearby Shell r_s. It may be written

$$n_s = \frac{a_0(1+\delta_s)^3}{R_0^3},$$

where a_0 is the value of a for zero red-shift. This number-density can be regarded as valid throughout the volume en-

L

closed within Shell r_s. Thus, for a shell of radius r greater than r_s, we may write

$$\frac{n}{n_s} = \frac{a(\delta)}{a_0} \left(\frac{1+\delta}{1+\delta_s}\right)^3 , \tag{12}$$

a ratio which no longer contains the (unknown) scale-factor R_0.

The number of sources in the whole of Shell r is $nR^3 dv$ which is simply $a(\delta)dv$. The mathematical theory of the model may be employed to convert dv into $\phi(\delta)d\delta$, where $\phi(\delta)$ is a function of the red-shift that is characteristic of each particular model universe, and $d\delta$ is the difference of the red-shift between the inner and outer radii of Shell r. The total number of sources counted by the observer as lying between his position and the shell for which the red-shift is δ is obtained by adding the contributions for all shells internal to the selected outermost one. This total is expressible as the integral

$$N = \int_0^\delta a(\delta) \, \phi(\delta) \, d\delta$$

and the rate of increase of N with δ is

$$\frac{dN}{d\delta} = a(\delta) \, \phi(\delta). \tag{13}$$

The classical 'minus three-halves' law for the variation of N with flux-density S implied that all the sources were of equal intrinsic radiative power and that the number-density was the same at all times. Thus the group of sources persists; no new ones appearing and none disappearing. The nearest approach to such a situation that can occur in a model universe is represented by a constant a. In this way the number-density changes only because of the expansion of the universe and there is no effect due to sources forming and dissolving again on their own. Hence in this case

$$\frac{n}{n_s} = \left(\frac{1+\delta}{1+\delta_s}\right)^3 . \tag{14}$$

The next step in the argument consists of remembering that, in a particular model universe, the flux-density of a source in Shell r can be expressed as a function of the red-

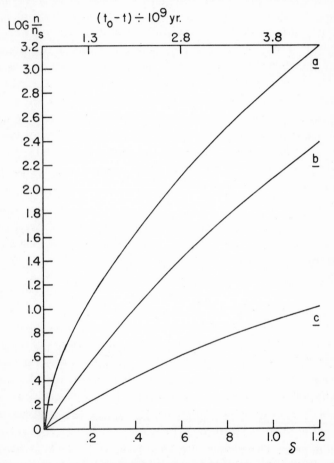

FIG. 17. Variation of number-density of Class II radio sources with red-shift in Milne's model.

shift [47]. If we then assume that N is proportional to $S^{-(3+\mu)/2}$, it will follow that N is a certain function of the red-shift involving the exponent $-\frac{1}{2}(3+\mu)$. Differentiation of this function with respect to the red-shift δ will give a formula for $dN/d\delta$ which must be equivalent to equation (13) for the particular model universe in question. In this way α is determined and its constancy or otherwise with respect to the red-shift can be discovered. The number-density ratio may then be found from equation (12) which, of course, reduces to equation (14) if α is a constant.

As an illustration, the computations have been carried out for Milne's model and a spectral index of -1. They are illustrated in fig. 17, the standard Shell r_s having been selected at the distance of the Virgo cluster whose red-shift is 0·004. Curve (a) reveals how n/n_s must vary in order that N shall be proportional to $S^{-1.65}$ as in the Australian survey. Curve (b) indicates the variation of n/n_s in order that the distribution of sources shall follow the 'minus three-halves' law in which $\mu=0$. It is only Curve (c) that corresponds to a constant α and which therefore is the true counterpart of the classical 'minus three-halves' law expressed by equation (2), Chapter 3. The predicted number-densities at $\delta=0·2$ from curves (a), (b) and (c) are in the ratios 12 : 3·5 : 1·7. The travel-times of the radiation, for various values of the red-shift, have also been calculated* for $H=130$ km/sec/mpc and are shown across the top of fig. 17. Hence, $1·3\times10^9$ years ago ($\delta=0·2$), there must have been about twice as many Class II radio sources as there are now if N is indeed proportional to $S^{-3/2}$. Any positive value of μ simply makes worse this excess of sources in the past. Thus the mere motion of the sources is insufficient to account for the empirical law, whether μ is equal to, or greater than, zero. There must also have been an intrinsic excess in

* The formula in Milne's model is $t_0-t=9·783\times10^{11}\dfrac{\delta}{H(1+\delta)}$ years.

the number of Class II radio sources as compared with the present time, i.e. relative to their number-density in the neighbourhood of our Galaxy. An interpretation of this excess has been proposed [50] on the hypothesis that all Class II radio sources are colliding galaxies. The theory is based on the idea that in the past, when all galaxies were closer together than they are now, collisions would be more frequent than they are at present. This is combined with the notion that collisions are short-lived events to predict that N should vary approximately like $S^{-1.65}$. Unfortunately for this theory, it has turned out that, as optical identifications of Class II radio sources have slowly accumulated, the number of sources which can be interpreted as galaxies in collision has not increased.

An escape from these difficulties may well be found in the future along different lines. In the discussion given above, it has been taken for granted that the 'minus three-halves' law of classical physics is somehow the expected one. Departures from it are supposed to retain the proportionality of N to *some constant power* of the flux-density. But this expectation is not borne out by the theory of the model universes. When α is constant, and there are thus no intrinsic changes of number-density, N is a far more complicated function of S than a simple power function.* It is true that for small red-shifts, the 'minus three-halves' law is approximately valid in all models, but this simplification soon vanishes. What this amounts to is that μ in the empirical exponent of S should be regarded as a variable that depends on the distance of the source rather than as a constant. The application of the

* Thus in Milne's model, N is proportional to

$$(1+\delta)^2 - \frac{1}{(1+\delta)^2} - 4\log(1+\delta)$$

whereas S is proportional to $(1+\delta)^{1+x}\delta^{-2}(2+\delta)^{-2}$. Hence for small red-shifts N is proportional to $S^{-3/2}$, but for large red-shifts, it approximates to $S^{-2/(3-x)}$.

method in practice is difficult, but not impossible; it would be most simply applied if we already had a good idea of which particular model universe to use. But with patience, and a liberal use of trial and error, the treatment may be capable of selecting a class of particular model universes that most nearly represent the counts of Class II radio sources without having recourse to intrinsic variations in their number-density.

Chapter 7

THE STEADY-STATE THEORY

The Model Universe

The general principles of the steady-state theory have been described earlier in this book, and they may be summarized in the statement that the world-picture of an observer is the same, wherever he may be located in space and time. The detailed consequences of this hypothesis must now be described. One immediate deduction is that the observed universe itself must possess the property of uniformity, as this was defined in Chapter 5. Moreover if it is agreed that at present a particular uniform model universe represents the observed universe, then this same model must hold throughout the history of the universe. The metric of the model will have the form exhibited in equation (1) of Chapter 5 and its precise expression may be obtained with the aid of the field equations (7) of Chapter 4. Hoyle's 1948 version [32] of these will be employed for the purpose because they are somewhat simpler than the later ones. It is also unfortunately the case that the difficulties and problems raised by the 1948 equations, which will be discussed presently, are also to be found in the 1960 versions. The field equations lead to the conclusion that the density and pressure of the representative gas are given by

$$8\pi G\rho = \frac{3kc^2}{R^2} + 3\left(\frac{R'}{R}\right)^2, \qquad (1)$$

$$8\pi G \frac{p}{c^2} = -\frac{2R''}{R} - \left(\frac{R'}{R}\right)^2 - \frac{kc^2}{R^2} + \frac{3c}{a}\frac{R'}{R}, \qquad (2)$$

wherein a is a constant which, it will be shown presently, is connected with the rate of creation of matter. The various terms in these equations may be evaluated individually by the following arguments. Consider first the Hubble parameter, which is the present value of the function R'/R. If this function varied with the time, then an ingenious astronomer could 'locate himself in time' by devising a method of measuring the function. Hence R'/R must be a constant of nature and it must be equal to h_1 – the value of the Hubble parameter today – throughout the history of the model universe. From this it follows that R is an exponential function of the time and that, if t_0 is the present moment and R_0 the value of R at time t_0, then $R = R_0 e^{h_1(t-t_0)}$. It also follows that the acceleration parameter R''/R is necessarily constant and is equal to h_1^2. Therefore the model universe of the steady-state theory predicts that the acceleration factor, q_0, must have the value -1 at all times.

In the second place, the only permissible value of the space-curvature constant k is zero because otherwise an observer could again locate himself in time by measuring the changes in kc^2/R^2. Thus the equations (1) and (2) become

$$8\pi G\rho = 3h_1^2,$$

$$8\pi G \frac{p}{c^2} = -3h_1^2 + \frac{3c}{a}h_1$$

and therefore the density and pressure of the representative gas are both constant. However, the pressure at the present time is zero and therefore it must always be zero. Consequently the constant a must be related to h_1 by $h_1 = c/a$. The complete specification of the steady-state model universe is therefore

$$R = R_0 e^{h_1(t-t_0)}, \quad k=0, \quad h_1 = \frac{c}{a}, \quad h_2 = h_1^2. \tag{3}$$

Mathematically therefore, the model is the same as the de Sitter universe of general relativity (equation (11) of Chapter 6), the constant a/c now playing the part of $(3/\lambda)^{1/2}$. But whereas Einstein's field equations indicated that the density and pressure in the de Sitter universe were both zero, the steady-state model universe has a zero pressure but a constant density given by

$$4\pi G\rho = 1\cdot5(c/a)^2 = 1\cdot5h_1^2. \tag{4}$$

As in the de Sitter universe the moment when $R=0$ occurs at an infinitely remote instant in the past. Hence if this instant is interpreted as the beginning of the expansion, the 'age of the universe' is infinitely long.

In the steady-state theory the galaxies are again represented by the special world-lines of the space-time. Thus their number-density may be calculated as was done for Class II radio sources. The same formulae apply except that n now refers to *all* galaxies and not merely to those which happen to be Class II radio sources. At the instant t the number-density in Shell r of fig. 11 is

$$n = \frac{\alpha(t)}{R^3(t)} = \frac{\alpha(t)}{R_0^3} e^{-3h_1(t-t_0)}.$$

This quantity must be independent of the time, otherwise the astronomer at O in fig. 11, by observing n, would again be able to locate himself in time. Thus α must be a variable and

$$\alpha(t) = \alpha_0 \, e^{3h_1 \, (t-t_0)}$$

where α_0 is a constant. It is involved in the number-density, n_s, inside the nearby Shell r_s, because $n_s = \alpha_0/R_0^3$.

At this point a limitation on the observational ingenuity of astronomers in a steady-state universe must be imposed. The observational methods they have invented must be deemed capable of measuring the Hubble parameter, the acceleration parameter, the average density of matter, the pressure and the number-density of galaxies. They find that all these quantities are constant in time. But they must not be able to devise a method of measuring a, because this function, which gives the intrinsic variation of the number-density, itself changes exponentially with the time. It was smaller in the past than it is now and will increase in magnitude in the future. Thus the basic concept of permanence in the midst of change would go by the board, and an observer would perceive a difference between his world-pictures at widely separated times, were he capable of measuring a. Clearly the same argument applies to R itself which must also remain inaccessible to observational measurement.

The new material needed to keep the density constant is created in the form of individual hydrogen atoms at rest relative to the already present matter in their immediate surroundings.* The rate of creation may be computed from the formula for a. Suppose that h_1 is expressed as the reciprocal of a time in years and that $(t-t_0)$ is one year. Thus a increases in one year by the factor e^{3h_1}. Therefore during the year, the intrinsic increase of mass in unit volume is equal to $(e^{3h_1}-1)$ times what it was at the beginning of the year. This factor is approximately equal to $3h_1$ because h_1 is very small compared with unity. In fact, if $H=75\,f$ km/sec/mpc, then $3h_1=2\cdot3\times10^{-10}\,f$ (year)$^{-1}$. The present average density of matter in galaxies is equal to the number-density of these objects multiplied by the mass of an average galaxy. It is equal to $\rho_0=3\cdot1\,f^2\times10^{-31}$ gr/cm^3 on Oort's computation. Thus in one year the number of newly-created hydrogen

* This was the original scheme [51]. In 1958 Gold and Hoyle [52] proposed that the new matter is created in the form of neutrons and that the 'cosmological material' is at a temperature of a thousand million degrees.

atoms in one cubic centimetre amounts to $3h_1\rho_0$ divided by the mass of a hydrogen atom, which is 1.673×10^{-24} gr. This implies that one hydrogen atom per year is created in a volume of 10 cubic kilometres, if $H=100$ km/sec/mpc, and in 2·4 cubic kilometres, if $H=160$ km/sec/mpc. Neither rate is directly observable, but nevertheless the determination of the creation-rate is uncertain because of the lack of precision in the values of the Hubble parameter and of the observed average density of matter.

Since the rate of creation of matter depends essentially on the quantity $3h_1$ and $h_1=c/a$, it is clear that the constant a in equation (2) does in fact represent the creation process.

Logical Difficulties

The steady-state theory raises a number of questions with regard to its internal consistency which must now be examined [53]. In the first place, there is the creation process itself which is defended on the ground that the law of conservation of mass and momentum is a small-scale law that need not hold in the large. Yet the laws of the propagation of light, the geodesic principle of general relativity and the laws of thermodynamics are accepted as universally valid in the steady-state theory. These laws are also small-scale laws established by experiments in the laboratory and by observations of bodies in the solar system and the Galaxy. Consistency would suggest that all physical laws, and not merely those of the conservation of mass and momentum, should be abandoned and a completely fresh start made. There is a contrast here with kinematical relativity in which E. A. Milne did indeed try to reconstruct the whole of mathematical physics from the basic ideas of his cosmology. In the steady-state theory, the principles by which certain physical laws are picked out for modification, whereas others are left unaltered, are not clear.

The second difficulty refers to the field equations (7) of Chapter 4. It will be remembered that, in Einstein's equations, the only reason for asserting that the Einstein and energy tensors were proportional to one another was that both independently satisfied a conservation law. But the energy-tensor now no longer satisfies such a law. The Einstein tensor continues to do so and therefore its presence in the field equations of the steady-state theory appears to be quite arbitrary and inexplicable.

A third problem is connected with gravitation which is usually discussed in terms of Newtonian ideas by the advocates of the steady-state theory. Granted that the newly-created matter may somehow be swept up into condensations that eventually become galaxies, there is still the infinitely long time-scale of the model universe to consider. An indefinitely large number of galaxies have been formed during the extremely remote past, others are more recent and yet others are being formed now. But in the volume occupied by an old galaxy, new matter has been created continually ever since the galaxy was formed. The gravitational field of the galaxy, it can easily be proved, will retain all this later material. Therefore, somewhere in the observed universe, there should be an indefinitely large number of old galaxies of extremely large mass. No such structures are observed and therefore they must be supposed to have moved so far from our own Galaxy as to be invisible. Nevertheless the world-picture obtainable from one of these 'invisible' old massive galaxies cannot be identical with that from a, presumably, young galaxy like our own. This appears to contradict the fundamental postulate of the theory which states that all world-pictures must be identical.

A fourth complication is introduced by the delicately balanced nature of the steady-state model universe. The method by which we have solved the field equations (1) and

(2) was a peculiar one. It consisted in computing the various terms occurring in the equations one at a time by means of considerations outside the equations themselves. The customary mathematical method of proceeding is different and may be illustrated thus: let it be granted that the pressure is always zero and that the space-curvature constant k is also zero. Then the scale-factor R satisfies the differential equation

$$2\frac{R''}{R} + \left(\frac{R'}{R}\right)^2 - 3\frac{c}{a}\frac{R'}{R} = 0.$$

Now the textbooks explain that an equation of this kind can be solved completely only if two 'initial conditions' are given. Let it be assumed that the time is measured from some arbitrarily selected moment in the past which is conventionally labelled $t=0$. The initial conditions may then be chosen to be the assertions that $R=1$ and $R'/R=Ac/a$ at $t=0$. Here A is an arbitrary constant. It then follows that R at any time t is related to its present value R_0 by

$$\left(\frac{R}{R_0}\right)^{3/2} = \frac{Ae^{\frac{3}{2}\frac{c}{a}t} - (A-1)}{Ae^{\frac{3}{2}\frac{c}{a}t_0} - (A-1)}.$$

From this, the Hubble and acceleration parameters and the density can be worked out. It proves to be the case that they are all time varying quantities and that therefore an unsteady-state universe has been predicted,* one which, however, degenerates into steadiness after an infinite time. But there is an exception to this statement: it occurs if, and only if, $A=1$, a condition that reproduces the steady-state universe solution

* The formulae for the Hubble parameter and the density are

$$\frac{R'}{R} = A\frac{c}{a}\left\{A - (A-1)\,e^{-\frac{3}{2}\frac{c}{a}t}\right\}^{-1},$$

$$8\pi G\,\rho = 3\left(\frac{c}{a}\right)^2 A^2\left\{A - (A-1)\,e^{-\frac{3}{2}\frac{c}{a}t}\right\}^{-2}.$$

(3). Hence a steady state is present only if the creation of matter constant a is related to the Hubble parameter at the zero of time by the precise equation $a=c/(R'/R)$. If, at this moment, a deviates slightly from this value, an unsteady state will result. To secure that nature operate with such mathematical exactitude might be a little difficult.

The Steady-State Theory and Observation

These difficulties of principle apart, an observational astronomer is still justified in asking if the steady-state model of the universe can give a satisfactory interpretation of cosmological data. All the theoretical apparatus of general relativity, in so far as the properties of radiation are concerned, is still applicable. Thus the theory of luminosity-distance, of distance by apparent size and the observational method of finding the Hubble and acceleration parameters employed in general relativity continue to hold but, of course, they now refer to the particular model specified by equations (3). The density, moreover, is now defined by equation (4).

In the steady-state model, the acceleration factor q_0 is necessarily equal to -1. But in Chapter 6, it was suggested that the observational value of this quantity lay between $+1$ and $+3$. Hence the prediction of the steady-state theory regarding the acceleration factor appears to contradict observation.

The predicted relationship between the quantity $4\pi G\rho$ and the square of the Hubble parameter is given by equation (4) and implies that the number σ_0 (see p. 142) has the exact value 1·5. Observation suggests that σ_0 is 0·044 which means that the density predicted by the steady-state model universe is 34 times too high. This also happened in the Einstein-de Sitter universe of general relativity, and was there attributed to the zero value of the cosmical constant. The omission of this constant from the field equations of the steady-state theory has not been compensated for by the introduction of the creation of matter terms. Therefore the steady-state model belongs to the class of models which predict what seems to be too high a density for the material content of the universe.

The number-density of Class II radio sources is necessarily constant in the steady-state universe, because otherwise an observer could locate himself in time by studying the manner in which the number-density changed. It will be remembered that the observed number, N, of Class II radio sources is proportional to the $-(3+\mu)/2$ power of the limiting flux-density, S (equation (5) of Chapter 3). In the steady-state theory, the analysis of the spatial distribution of sources, already given for the general relativity models, continues to hold. This leads to the conclusion that the empirical relation between N and S necessarily implies a time-varying number-density for Class II radio sources.* Thus the distribution in space of these sources, as far as the presently available data go, appears to be out of harmony with the steady-state requirement.

The same kind of difficulty arises with respect to clusters of galaxies, if Just's analysis [54] of Abell's work is accepted. Just noticed that those clusters which were remote – as judged by the apparent magnitude of the tenth brightest cluster member – tended to be richer also. Thus, distance being an index of the date in the past at which the cluster is observed, the richness depends on time. Therefore this property of clusters of galaxies also fails to satisfy the steady-state requirement.

These considerations taken together hardly encourage the

* From the point of view of the observer at O in fig. 11, the number-density would have to vary with the red-shift according to the formula

$$\frac{n.}{n_s}=\left(\frac{1+\delta}{1+\delta_s}\right)^{\frac{7-3x+\mu(1-x)}{2}}\left(\frac{\delta}{\delta_s}\right)^{\mu}\frac{2+(3-x)\delta}{2+(3-x)\delta_s}.$$

It is impossible to select values of the constants x and μ which would make n/n_s independent of δ.

belief that the steady-state theory describes the observed universe. Most of the difficulties it encounters would also arise in general relativity if one particular model universe were to be selected on *a priori* grounds as the 'correct' one, for example, if the Einstein-de Sitter universe were to be chosen as the only possible one because of its mathematical simplicity and because it assumes that the cosmical constant is zero. But in addition to difficulties introduced in this way, the steady-state theory further restricts the possibilities by requiring that every essential large-scale feature of the universe must be unchanged with the passage of time. This extreme specialization greatly increases the risk that the steady-state theory will run counter to observation. Be this as it may, it does share one virtue with its predecessor kinematical relativity: the steady-state theory has given rise to much controversy. Cosmologists in consequence have been forced to refine and make precise their ideas whether they work in general relativity or in one of the alternative theories. And this, in the present state of cosmological studies, is of benefit to all.

Chapter 8

A SUMMARY IN CONCLUSION

We have seen that cosmology, when due regard is paid to the observational data, is a more complex subject than is sometimes realized. The question of what is meant by distance in the universe is one of great intricacy and uncertainty, not only because of the presence of errors of measurement, but also because of difficulties of principle. We have concluded that the distances of remote galaxies, expressed in hundreds of millions of light-years, are so ambiguous that their employment is best avoided. The same is true of the equally great time intervals during which light is said to have travelled from remote objects. Therefore in using theory to interpret the available astronomical data it has been thought best to work with directly observable quantities rather than with derivative notions such as distance or the travel-time of radiation. The observables are: the red-shift in the lines of the spectra of galaxies; the optical apparent magnitudes of galaxies; the flux-densities of those galaxies which are radio sources; the numbers of galaxies; the diameters of extra-galactic radio sources; and the characteristics of clusters of galaxies.

The theory of cosmology to which most attention has been paid is that derived from Einstein's general relativity. This theory takes account of the effects of the high speeds evidenced by the red-shift and also of the effects of gravitation. Emphasis has been placed on the fact that the relativistic models of the universe are highly idealized and simplified

M

representations of the observed universe. This artificiality is not a consequence of the theory itself; rather is it a result of the search for the mathematically simplest description. The great uniformity and homogeneity attributed to the material content of a model universe, though it gives insight into the constitution of the observed universe, must make us careful in drawing too many conclusions about the remote past from such models. A variety of models is seen to be possible, differing from one another in two ways: on the one hand, they show that different kinds of motions of expansion, accelerated, retarded or of constant speed, can occur. On the other, they show that space may be of finite or of infinite extent. Comparison of the predictions of these models with the red-shift observations presently available suggests that the expansion of the universe is being retarded at present. These data also suggest that the value of the cosmical constant is negative, which means that in addition to gravitation there is another universal retarding force present in the universe. That space is of infinite extent is also indicated. It is probably along the lines of more intensive study of the red-shifts that progress in the next few years will be most likely to yield results. Not only are measurements of very large red-shifts of interest; there is also scope for work in completing our picture of the march of red-shift against apparent magnitude for galaxies in clusters within the range already investigated. Counts of galaxies that are radio sources (Class II radio sources), made to increasingly lower limits of flux-density, should also give valuable additional information. The same can be said of measurements of angular diameter for radio sources of this kind.

Two alternative theories of cosmology, which contrast with general relativity, have also been described. They are kinematical relativity, which is only briefly touched on, and the steady-state theory. Both theories have in common the postulate that homogeneity and uniformity are necessary properties of the universe and that it cannot be thought of in any other way. Both attempt to describe the nature of the universe first of all and then to introduce a theory of gravitation. In this respect they have so far failed to produce convincing gravitational theories. The steady-state theory also abandons the notion of the conservation of mass and energy, a principle that is experimentally well grounded in terrestrial laboratory physics. Kinematical relativity predicts that the motion of expansion can neither be retarded nor accelerated, the steady-state theory, that it must necessarily be accelerated. These conclusions appear to be in conflict with the available data on red-shifts.

The view of the author of this book is that an observational proof of the validity of some highly specific model of the universe, whether it be a general relativity model or the specific model of kinematical relativity or the equally specialized one of the steady-state theory, is unlikely to be forthcoming for a very long time. In the foreseeable future, progress will more probably lie in the progressive exclusion of certain models from consideration. We may thus hope to arrive one day at some small, closely related group of models from which we may understand the precise nature of the expansion of the system of galaxies and the geometrical character of space.

APPENDIX

Table A: The 18 Clusters of Humason, Mayall and Sandage

Cluster Number	Cluster Designation	δ	m	y	m_c	z
1	Virgo	·004	9·17	61·2230	9·16	61·2130
2	Perseus 0316+4121	·018	12·59	61·3770	12·51	61·2970
3	Coma 1257+2812	·022	12·94	61·2915	12·84	61·1915
4	Hercules 1603+1755	·036	14·28	61·6400	14·12	61·4800
5	2308+0720	·043	14·95	61·8760	14·78	61·6760
6	2322+1425	·044	15·25	62·0960	15·04	61·8860
7	1145+5559	·052	15·95	62·4335	15·71	62·1935
8	0106−1536	·053	15·46	61·9020	15·21	61·6520
9	1024+1039	·065	16·19	62·1890	15·88	61·8720
10	1239+1852	·072	15·55	61·3270	15·22	60·9970
11	Cor. Bor. 1520+2754	·072	16·26	62·0370	15·93	61·7070
12	0705+3506	·078	16·63	62·2330	16·26	61·8630
13	Boötes 1431+3146	·131	17·92	62·3970	17·31	61·7870
14	1055+5702	·134	17·94	62·3680	17·31	61·7380
15	0025+2223	·159	18·13	62·1865	17·39	61·4465
16	0138+1840	·173	17·97	61·8435	17·16	61·0335
17	0925+2044	·192	18·44	62·0870	17·54	61·1870
18	Hydra 0855+0321	·202	18·78	62·3165	17·84	61·3765

The red-shifts are taken from Humason, Mayall and Sandage, *Astron. J.* **61**, 97, 1956, except that the red-shift for cluster No. 4 incorporates the measurements of Burbidge and Burbidge, *Astrophys. J.* **130**, 629, 1959.

The apparent magnitude of the synthetic brightest cluster member, m, is corrected for obscuration to the galactic pole. Thus $m = m_1 + 0·25$ where m_1 is taken from *Hd. der Physik*, **53**, 445, Tab. 12. In calculating the Hubble parameter from the value of A in, for example, equ. (4) of Chapter 6, the absolute magnitude M must also be increased by 0·25.

The apparent magnitudes m_c are the $\bar{P}_c$ of Tab. XIII of the paper by Humason, Mayall and Sandage.

The value of c used in calculating y and z is $9·711 \times 10^{-9}$ parsec/sec since h_1 is in sec^{-1} and D is in parsecs.

Table B: Abell's 18 Clusters

Cluster Number	Cluster Designation	δ	m	z
3	Coma 1257+2812	·022	13·5	61·8515
8	0106−1536	·053	15·0	61·4420
9	1024+1039	·065	16·0	61·9990
11	Cor. Bor. 1520+2754	·072	15·6	61·3770
12	0705+3506	·078	15·4	61·0030
19	0348+0613	·085	17·7	63·1165
20	1513+0433	·094	16·0	61·1980
13	Boötes 1431+3146	·131	17·0	61·4770
14	1055+5702	·134	17·0	61·4280
21	2253+2341	·143	17·1	61·3870
22	1534+3749	·153	17·0	61·6400
15	0025+2223	·159	17·7	61·7565
16	0138+1840	·173	17·9	61·7735
23	1309−0105	·175	17·6	61·4485
24	1304+3110	·183	17·7	61·4510
17	0925+2044	·192	17·7	61·3470
25	1253+4422	·198	17·7	61·2800
18	Hydra 0855+0321	·202	17·7	61·2365

The photo-red magnitudes are taken from G. O. Abell, *Astrophys. J. Suppl.* **3**, 211, Tab. 3 and are corrected for obscuration to the pole. The calculation of z is carried out as for the data of Tab. A.

Table C: Clusters observed photoelectrically by Baum

Cluster Number	Cluster Designation	δ	m_c	z
1	Virgo	·004	9·2	61·25
3	Coma 1257+2812	·022	12·8	61·15
11	Cor. Bor. 1520+2754	·072	15·6	61·38
14	1055+5702	·134	16·9	61·33
17	0925+2044	·192	17·4	61·05
26	0024+1654	·29	18·7	61·43
27	1448+2617	·35	18·5	60·88
28	1410+5224	·46	19·3	61·06

REFERENCES AND NOTES

The following references and notes are intended for those readers who may wish to have additional information on points raised in the text. Unless otherwise stated, all the works quoted are written in English.

1. G. M. CLEMENCE, *Science*, **123**, 567, 1956.
2. J. DUFAY, *Galactic Nebulae and Interstellar Matter*, Philosophical Library: New York, 1957.
3. C. S. BEALS and J. B. OKE, *Mon. Not. Roy. Astron. Soc.*, **113**, 530, 1953.
4. CECILIA PAYNE GAPOSCHKIN, *The Galactic Novae*, p. 13. North Holland Pub. Co.: Amsterdam. Interscience Pub.: New York, 1957.
5. G. DE VAUCOULEURS, *Astron. J.*, **64**, 397, 1959.
6. H. C. ARP, *Astron. J.*, **63**, 45, 1958. The author is greatly indebted to Dr. Arp for his kindness in supplying the details from which fig. 6 was plotted.
7. A. R. SANDAGE, *Astrophys. J.*, **127**, 513, 1958.
8. S. VAN DEN BERGH, *J. Roy. Astron. Soc. Canada*, **54**, 49, 1960.
9. Computations by the author using the $\dot{m}$ in Tab. I of S. C. B. GASCOIGNE and O. J. EGGEN (*Mon. Not. Roy. Astron. Soc.*, **117**, 430, 1957) and the periods in A. BLAAUW and H. R. MORGAN (*Bull. Astron. Inst. Netherlds.*, **12**, 95, 1954). The symbol m stands for both $\dot{m}$ and P_E. Conversions from P_E to B ($=m'$) are made using a formula in Sec. 3 of H. C. ARP (*Astron. J.*, **63**, 45, 1958) and (6) of O. J. EGGEN (*Astron. J.*, **60**, 65, 1955). The group averages for m and $\log P$ are obtained by omitting the largest value in each case for the 17 stars.
10. H. C. ARP, *Astron. J.*, **61**, 15, 1956.
11. T. SCHMIDT, *Z. Astrophysik*, **41**, 182, 1957 (in German).
12. G. C. MCVITTIE, *Handbuch der Physik*, **53**, 445. Springer: Berlin, 1959.
13. E. HOLMBERG, *Med. Lunds Astron. Obs.*, Ser. II, No. 136, 1958.
14. C. D. SHANE and co-workers, *Astron. J.*, **59**, 285, 1954; **61**, 292, 1956; **64**, 197, 1959.
15. F. ZWICKY, *Handbuch der Physik*, **53**, 390. Springer: Berlin, 1959.

16. J. NEYMAN, E. L. SCOTT and C. D. SHANE, *Astrophys. J.*, **117**, 92, 1952. Also *Handbuch der Physik*, **53**, 416. Springer: Berlin, 1959.

17. E. P. HUBBLE, *Astrophys. J.*, **84**, 517, 1936.

18. F. ZWICKY, *Morphological Astronomy*, Sec. 20e. Springer: Berlin, 1957.

19. J. H. OORT, *La Structure et l'Evolution de l'Univers*, p. 163. Stoops: Brussels, 1958.

20. G. O. ABELL, *Astrophys. J. Suppl.*, **3**, 211, 1958.

21. M. L. HUMASON, N. U. MAYALL and A. R. SANDAGE, *Astron. J.*, **61**, 97, 1956.

22. B. Y. MILLS, O. B. SLEE and E. R. HILL, *Austr. J. Phys.*, **11**, 360, 1958.

23. D. W. DEWHIRST, *Paris Symposium on Radio Astronomy*, p. 507. University Press: Stanford, 1959.

24. D. O. EDGE, J. R. SHAKESHAFT, W. B. MCADAM, J. E. BALDWIN and S. ARCHER, *Mem. Roy. Astron. Soc.*, **68**, 37, 1959.

25. R. MINKOWSKI and O. C. WILSON, *Astrophys. J.*, **123**, 373, 1956.

26. O. C. WILSON, *Publ. Astron. Soc. Pacific*, **61**, 132, 1949.

27. J. STEBBINS and A. E. WHITFORD, *Astrophys. J.*, **108**, 413, 1948.

28. G. R. WHITFIELD, *Paris Symposium on Radio Astronomy*, p. 297. University Press: Stanford, 1959.

29. A. EINSTEIN, *The Meaning of Relativity*. Methuen: London, 1950.
H. DINGLE, *The Special Theory of Relativity*. Methuen: London, 1946.
P. COUDERC, *The Expansion of the Universe*. Macmillan: New York, 1952.
M. K. MUNITZ, *Space, Time and Creation*. Free Press: Glencoe, Illinois, 1957.
See also the works quoted in Ref. 33.

30. E. A. MILNE, *Relativity, Gravitation and World Structure*. Clarendon Press: Oxford, 1935.
G. J. WHITROW, *The Structure and Evolution of the Universe*. Hutchinson: London. Harper: New York, 1959.

31. H. BONDI, *Cosmology*. University Press: Cambridge, 1952.
F. HOYLE, *La Structure et l'Evolution de l'Univers*, p. 53. Stoops: Brussels, 1958.

32. F. HOYLE, *Mon. Not. Roy. Astron. Soc.*, **108**, 372, 1948 and **120**, 256, 1960.

33. The detailed mathematical proofs of the statements made in this chapter will be found in G. C. MCVITTIE, *General Relativity and Cosmology*, Chapman and Hall: London, 1956, Chps. 8 and 9.

See also R. C. TOLMAN, *Relativity, Thermodynamics and Cosmology*, Clarendon Press: Oxford, 1934, Sections 133–165.

34. H. P. ROBERTSON, *Publ. Astron. Soc. Pacific*, **67**, 82, 1955.

35. See H. P. ROBERTSON, Ref. (34), Equ. (10b).—G. C. MCVITTIE, Ref. (1), Sec. 8:5.—W. H. MCCREA, *Z. Astrophys.*, **9**, 290, 1934–35. Equ. (15).—O. HECKMANN, *Theorien der Kosmologie*, Equ. (69b). Springer: Berlin, 1942 (in German).

36. H. BONDI, *Cosmology*, Equ. (10.21′). University Press: Cambridge, 1952.

37. W. A. BAUM, *Astron. J.*, **62**, 5, 1957. W. A. BAUM and R. MINKOWSKI, *Astron. J.*, **65**, 483, 1960. R. MINKOWSKI, *Publ. Astron. Soc. Pacific*, **72**, 354, 1960.

38. ELIZABETH L. SCOTT, *Astron. J.*, **62**, 248, 1957.
J. NEYMAN and E. L. SCOTT, *Handbuch der Physik*, **53**, 416. Springer: Berlin, 1959.

39. F. HOYLE and A. R. SANDAGE, *Publ. Astron. Soc. Pacific*, **68**, 301, 1956.

40. J. H. OORT, *La Structure et l'Evolution de l'Univers*, p. 163. Stoops: Brussels, 1958. See also C. W. ALLEN, *Astrophysical Quantities*, p. 240. Athlone Press: London, 1955. Allen takes $H=$ 290 km/sec/mpc; his range of density, converted to $H=75$ km/sec/ mpc, is $2 \cdot 1 \times 10^{-31}$ to $2 \cdot 1 \times 10^{-30}$ gr./cm³. The chief advocate of a high density is F. ZWICKY (*Morphological Astronomy*, Sec. 3.6. Springer: Berlin, 1957) who proposes a density of not less than $1 \cdot 8 \times 10^{-28}$ gr/cm³, on Oort's distance scale. Zwicky himself uses a scale in which $H=550$ km/sec/mpc. He appears to place too much stress on conditions inside dense clusters of galaxies and on his theory of the dynamics of galaxies within such clusters.

41. W. DE SITTER, *Bull. Astron. Inst. Netherlands*, **5**, 211, 1930.

42. O. HECKMANN and E. SCHUCKING, *La Structure et l'Evolution de l'Univers*, p. 149. Stoops: Brussels, 1958. *Observatory*, **79**, 130, 1959.

43. A. L. ZELMANOV, *Proceedings of the Sixth Conference on Problems of Cosmogony*, p. 144. Acad. Sci. USSR: Moscow, 1959 (in Russian).

44. H. BONDI, *Cosmology*, Sec. 9.4. University Press: Cambridge, 1952.

45. G. C. MCVITTIE and S. P. WYATT, *Astrophys. J.*, **130**, 1, 1959.

46. J. C. PECKER and E. SCHATZMAN, *Astrophysique Generale*, p.611. Masson: Paris, 1959 (in French).

47. The results are obtained by using equations (5), (7), 15) and (17) of Chapter 5. They are as follows:

(a) Milne's model:

$$\frac{D}{D_s} = \frac{\delta(1+\tfrac{1}{2}\delta)}{\delta_s(1+\tfrac{1}{2}\delta_s)},$$

$$\frac{S}{S_s} = \frac{\delta_s{}^2(2+\delta_s)^2}{(1+\delta_s)^{1+x}} \quad \frac{(1+\delta)^{1+x}}{\delta^2(2+\delta)^2};$$

(b) Einstein–de Sitter model:

$$\frac{D}{D_s} = \frac{\left\{(1+\delta)^{1/2}-1\right\}}{\left\{(1+\delta_s)^{1/2}-1\right\}} \frac{(1+\delta)^{1/2}}{(1+\delta_s)^{1/2}},$$

$$\frac{S}{S_s} = \frac{\left\{(1+\delta_s)^{1/2}-1\right\}^2}{(1+\delta_s)^x} \frac{(1+\delta)^x}{\left\{(1+\delta)^{1/2}-1\right\}^2}.$$

(c) de Sitter universe (also valid for the steady-state theory):

$$\frac{D}{D_s} = \frac{\delta(1+\delta)}{\delta_s(1+\delta_s)},$$

$$\frac{S}{S_s} = \frac{\delta_s{}^2(1+\delta_s)^{1-x}}{\delta^2(1+\delta)^{1-x}}.$$

The suffix s denotes quantities referring to the standard source.

48. G. C. MCVITTIE, *General Relativity and Cosmology*, Sec. 8.5. Chapman and Hall: London, 1956. F. HOYLE, *Paris Symposium on Radio Astronomy*, p. 529. University Press: Stanford, 1959.

49. G. C. MCVITTIE, *Proceedings of the Symposium 'Les Theories Relativistes de la Gravitation,'* (in press)

50. W. PRIESTER, *Z. Astrophysik*, **46**, 179, 1958 (in German).

51. H. BONDI, *Cosmology*, Sec. 12.6. University Press: Cambridge, 1952.

52. T. GOLD and F. HOYLE, *Paris Symposium on Radio Astronomy*, p. 583. University Press: Stanford, 1959.

53. G. J. WHITROW, *The Structure and Evolution of the Universe*, pp. 142–8. Hutchinson: London. Harper: New York, 1959.

54. K. JUST, *Astrophys. J.*, **129**, 268, 1959.

INDEX